The curative power of flowers and plants

Aromatherapy

Anna Huete

Practical guide to essential oils
for body, mind, and spirit

KONECKY&KONECKY

KONECKY & KONECKY
72 AYERS POINT RD.
OLD SAYBROOK, CT 06475
VISIT US ON THE WEB AT WWW.KONECKYANDKONECKY.COM

© Anna Huete, 2007

© Editorial Océano, S. L., 2007 — Grupo Océano
English translation © 2013 Konecky & Konecky, LLC.

Translated from the Spanish by Janet Foster

ISBN: 978-1-56852-798-7

Photography: JOHANN WOLF, CORBIS, FIRO FOTO, GETTY, ARCHIVO OCÉANO
Models: NATHALIE LE GOSLES
Design: JORDI GALEANO
Art direcrtion: MONTSE VILARNAU

Printed in China

Contents

Essential oils for the body

Essential oils for the soul

Introduction to essential oils

Nature: fountain of wellbeing

Nature provides great treasures for health and wellbeing, which humans have known how to harness for thousands of years. To feel well — without hunger, without cold, and without illness — has been a priority for mankind since the beginning of time. In order to reach this difficult objective, civilizations have availed themselves of the tools and remedies that plants have placed at their fingertips.

Water, pure air, and the earth facilitate the growth of countless species of plants that contain within them a great secret: essential oils. Since ancient times these have been used in an almost intuitive way, and in each case, scientific research has confirmed that they contain a broad spectrum of active therapeutic ingredients.

These essential oils— pure, volatile, and rich in properties and perfumes— form the basis of aromatherapy. This book is not about using them as perfume, but rather as a means to attain physical and emotional equilibrium.

A pleasing, fragrant massage, a warm and relaxing bath, an aroma that envelops your home: these are some of the ways to apply aromatherapy. It's appealing, isn't it?

Using essential oils provides a perfect excuse to care for your body and mind and to devote a little time to slowing down the accelerated pace that is all too often part and parcel of daily life.

In the following pages, we are going to highlight the pleasure of using aromatherapy to feel better. We will explain to you how to identify and acquire essential oils, and the best ways to apply them for maximum benefit. You will discover how nice it feels to pamper yourself and how simple it can be to find relief for a range of ailments or for when you are feeling low.

We cannot promise you health, beauty, and happiness, but we can assure you that by choosing this path, one that begins with you, you will have at your fingertips one of the most satisfying natural therapies in existence: aromatherapy.

The therapeutic power of aromatherapy

The active principles in essential oils have potent curative effects for the body and for negative emotions. The process stems from chemical components with proven therapeutic benefits that on many occasions have been synthesized in laboratories and converted into pharmaceuticals. The use of essential oils in aromatherapy, however, is based on natural principles, and they penetrate your body in different ways depending on how you apply them. They are very volatile, and

can be administered through the olfactory system, by means of direct inhalation or a diffuser. On a molecular level, these oils can also penetrate the pores of your skin during a bath or massage. In the first case they are administered directly to the brain and limbic system, and in the second, through the bloodstream.

Olfactory health

When we are small, one of the best ways to get information is through our sense of smell.

A newborn baby has blurred vision and hears muffled noises but captures to perfection the smell of its mother, which reassures the baby while in its mother's lap, or nursing. Smells unconsciously inform us of what happens by transmitting information to the brain, which, in turn, generates responses.

In today's world, it may seem that the sense of smell is losing its importance, but this is not true. It is clearly no longer a necessity for subsistence, as was the case in the past. We don't

use it to escape predators, or to be alerted to danger by the particular aroma of a toxic plant. But it is present in our life and, on some occasions, certainly modifies our unconscious behavior by generating feelings of wellbeing or sadness. It helps us to feel better or makes us irritable. It ultimately influences and affects us.

Say someone in your house is baking those delicious cookies that your grandmother used to make when you were a child, it is very likely that in a matter of seconds the sweet aroma will take you back to recall those days of your childhood and warm memories of that time. Nostalgia will overtake you, and you won't be able to resist smiling. None of our senses has as much power to be evocative — and as potent — as the olfactory. Those famous pheromones, the hormones of sexual attraction secreted by females of many species, including human beings, have the power to attract a male unconsciously through aroma. This chemical message is captured by the brain through the olfactory sense, determining behavior and also a series of physical reactions.

One of the principles of aromatherapy is simply this: it generates certain physical effects through the aromas of essential oils that come through our sense of smell to the brain. This process begins in the nasal mucosa, where the aromatic particles dissolve and are disseminated by means of the volatility characteristic of essential oils. That is to say, the aroma evaporates extraordinarily rapidly. In the nasal mucosa, which in medicine is also called "olfactory epithelium," are millions of chemoreceptor cells that capture the scent. From there, the scent travels through the rear base of the epithelium and reaches the nerve fibers, where, by virtue of nerve impulses, it is carried to the palate and cranial cavity. Once there, and in a matter of tenths of a second, it reaches the olfactory bulb, a part of the brain, and from there, the limbic system.

This system is one of the most important regions of the brain, since it is responsible for managing instincts, memory and vital functions. When the limbic system "receives" the active ingredients of essential oils, it initiates an immediate response and releases chemicals that end up in the nervous system, which is good for either stimulation or relaxation. Since our nervous system is distributed throughout every nook and cranny of our body, aromatherapy can, through the smell, relieve pain or reduce stress. Simple and effective, at the same time, it's complicated and apparently inexplicable.

Furthermore, when smelling or inhaling an aroma, particles of essential oils reach the lungs and, through them, our circulatory system. Therefore diffusers, inhalers and smelling a few drops of essential oil on a handkerchief or on our pillow have a dual effect on the nervous system and the bloodstream; both are fundamental to our internal system. At the same

What is aromatherapy?

The natural health technique called "aromatherapy" has been so named for less than a century. However, for at least a thousand years, in different cultures and societies, essential oils have been used in therapeutic techniques, for spiritual purposes, and for cosmetics. In reality, the terms "essential oil" and "aromatherapy" are often used too broadly. They have nothing to do with perfumery, and they are sometimes used as words that sound natural in order to better market cosmetics.

In reality, as its name indicates, aromatherapy is a therapy that utilizes aromas and seeks to improve our health in daily life, whether it be the health of the body or the mind. However, it is not based solely on scents, but on a whole combination of chemical components of essential oils extracted from plants. As we will see, there are several methods of application, including inhalation, which apply only to pure essential oils.

The term is originally French: *aromathérapie.* Conceived by René-Maurice Gattefossé, a French chemist, this term clearly expressed the concept of affecting a cure through aromas. However, that definition can lead us to think that it is just about inhaling essential oils, which lends itself to an association with perfumery. In reality, essential oils work in many other ways, as explained in our discussion of the olfactory sense, that don't have only to do with what smells good or bad.

Like many other natural therapies, aromatherapy does not utilize medicine and does not seek solely to counteract ailments. The goal goes beyond to a holistic approach that aims to preserve, maintain, and enhance the body and soul, and to prevent possible diseases. The tools are essential oils that by means of various application techniques help us to heal ourselves, to regenerate, and to regain equilibrium.

time, the sedative or stimulating effect of essential oils also directly affects our mood, since it takes place in the brain where our emotions are born.

As you can begin to sense, aromatherapy can be the catalyst for a broad range of health benefits, and it is always pleasurable. And, above all, it's holistic, because it affects your body and emotions.

Absorb health

One of the most common ways to apply essential oils is on our skin, either with a massage or a hot bath. In the first case they are added to vegetable oil in order to be diluted, since they are very powerful. In the second, just ten drops are enough, mixed with the bath water. When applied in this way, the active principles of essential oils, their tiny molecules, penetrate our pores. From there they pass through the tiny capillaries under our skin and continue on to be incorporated into our circulatory system. The rest of the journey is easy to imagine since the bloodstream travels throughout our organs, muscles, skin, and finally our whole body. As soon as they are incorporated into the circulatory system, the active ingredients of essential oils travel to areas that need it or to organs for which they may provide greater therapeutic benefits. It is a topical application, effective at two levels since, in addition to penetrating our skin, it also reaches our nose. Aromatherapy penetrates our bodies rapidly and comprehensively.

The Application of aromatherapy

The application of aromatherapy with its great benefits can be practiced in a variety of ways for health and wellbeing. It can be used, for example, in consultation with a physician or psychologist and, of course, while reclining during a session with a beautician. In addition, it very effectively complements treatments used by many naturopaths, chiropractors and physiotherapists.

On the other hand, one of its great advantages is that it can be used at home—in the bath, for giving a massage, as perfume, or to cleanse your environment. It can also help your little ones sleep better and ultimately improve the quality of your physical and emotional states.

In this book we will provide a clear and reader-friendly explanation of the primary applications, and how you can employ them. Moreover, we will give you information about the most commonly used essential oils and their characteristics. Don't forget that it is always important to consult a specialist and that "aromatherapy at home" complements the benefits of a consultation or a visit to a health professional. Whatever the case, it is always a subtle and pleasant therapy that employs completely natural components, and one that seeks, through active principles, to improve our physical equilibrium and energy. A massage, a bath, a diffuser are some of the pleasant applications that you will discover, if you devote a little time to forgetting stress and slowing down. You will find that there is a whole fountain of wellbeing at your fingertips. You will not regret taking advantage of it for your own benefit and for that of those who are close to you.

From prehistoric to modern times

Although, as we have told you, the practice of aromatherapy has only been identified as such for a few decades, the use of plants and their derivatives in daily life as a remedy for ailments and for overcoming emotional difficulties has been practiced almost since the dawn of humankind.

For thousands of years, medicinal plants were the only resource used by different cultures to affect curative remedies and for cosmetics. However, the twentieth century brought with it the development of chemistry and the capacity to synthesize the main active ingredients of plants in the laboratory. With this came the creation of synthetic medicines and the development of the pharmaceutical industry and modern medicine to which humanity owes a great debt. As a result, illnesses that were incurable for centuries can be cured, infections above all.

However, the great success of conventional medicine diminished respect for natural remedies, even though for thousands of years they had played an important role. Forgetting this led to the virtual ostracism of many natural therapies, which nonetheless never disappeared. Today society is returning to a true appreciation of their efficacy. Doctors, researchers, and pharmacists from all over the world are once again interested in natural remedies and medicinal plants. In addition, many patients consider it to be the best option for curing or relieving the most common ailments and avoid resorting to drugs with their side effects. This in part explains that the current trend in treatment is to combine both of the existing forms to reach a single goal: our wellbeing.

Fire and wood

There is evidence that for thousands of years mankind has harnessed the power of medicinal plants and also some types of wood. The discovery of fire was a decisive turning point that had far reaching benefits, among them the power of smoke from plants. Although medicinal applications have been gradually discovered over millennia, very early on mankind began to use the smoke from different types of wood to achieve certain therapeutic effects or to influence moods. (One may surmise that since there were no trees with aromatic resin in Europe, the first human settlers used herbs, like rosemary or thyme, to make incense.)

In the course of burning wood, primitive peoples saw that different effects were produced, such as drowsiness, happiness, anger, or even spiritual effects. They concluded that smoke ex-

Did you know…?

● *Prehistoric man used plants not only as a source of food, but also to cure ailments and for performing religious rituals. No small number of archeological and burial sites contain remains of therapeutic plants.*

pelled bad spirits from the body, allowing health to return.

For this reason, since the beginning of time, fuming the body with smoke has been used as a method for healing the sick. It is a therapy that is still found in some cultures, not so remote from us as you might think. In fact, it was used in France until only a few decades ago.

Science has demonstrated that the therapeutic effect is real, and not just superstition. The scientific basis for the curative power of smoke of certain woods stems from its antiseptic and antibacterial properties. However, for primitive peoples, its healing capabilities resided in fragrances that placated the gods or spirits responsible for the wellbeing of the individual and the community.

This practice was maintained over thousands of years within many belief systems. Incense has been the type of wood most commonly used for its "miracle smoke," and is still used today as a meditation aid in various religions such as Buddhism, Hinduism, and Catholicism.

India and Ayurveda

Plants form the basis for Hindu medicine, which has a history of more than four thousand years. This medicine is called "Ayurveda" (meaning "the

laws of health"). It uses up to seven hundred substances, among which plants predominate by far. Among them are cinnamon, tuberose, ginger, myrrh, coriander, and sandalwood.

Herbal remedies, which have been found described in numerous Sanskrit manuscripts of great beauty, were widely used and were the basis of curative formulas, invocations to the gods, and religious cults.

The third-century Buddhist King Ashoka classified a great number of medicinal plants that are still in use today. The majority of these have been incorporated into different drugs and, of course, aromatherapy. These include fenugreek,

Did you know...?

● *In the Indo-Aryan language, the single word "atar" was used as a term for "smoke," "wind," "odor" and "essence." A cognate of that word found its way into English, where we speak of "attar of roses," or other plants.*

caraway, pepper, cardamom, ginger, cloves, nutmeg, sandalwood, benzoin, hemp, castor, sesame, and aloe.

Ancient Egypt

The ancient Egyptians knew a great deal about medicine, and plants formed the basis for many of their natural remedies. In addition, they drew from the vegetable kingdom to create unguents for worshipping their gods, for mummification, and for veneration of beauty and the body. Aromatherapy was part of daily life, present in rituals, astrology, medicine, and cosmetics. It was essential to the daily life of the upper classes. Egyptian priests and doctors were very knowledgeable about the world of perfumes. They knew that some could be intoxicating, and also could lead to insanity. Because of this, certain hallucinogenic essences were used to protect Pharaoh's tombs from thieves. Anyone inhaling these aromas would suffer monstrous hallucinations, creating the belief that this was the revenge of the gods.

Priests were in charge of creating sacred incense that was burned to honor the gods. They used up to twenty ingredients, in particular myrrh, juniper, cassia, saffron, cinnamon, and tuberose.

Herbs were also used medicinally. Evidence of this is found in the *Ebers Papyrus*, a famous XVIII-

Did you know...?

● When Tutankhamen's tomb was opened in 1922, 35 alabaster perfumers were found containing perfume with scent that could still be perceived, after millennia, including frankincense and myrrh.

Fresco from the Tomb of Sethi I (British Museum). Burning incense in front of Osiris

dynasty scroll, twenty meters long, that includes more than eight hundred recipes and medical remedies, almost all of plant origin. For example, as a cure for hay fever it suggests using a mixture of aloe, myrrh, antimony and honey.

The other major use of aromatherapy was in the art of embalming, used with the aim of preserving corpses. Remnants of plants with antiseptic properties, such as galbanum, clove, cinnamon, and nutmeg, have been found on the bandages.

Mesopotamia

Ancient medicines were also germinated and developed in the Mesopotamian kingdoms, situated between the Tigris and the Euphrates.

These mainly comprised vegetable substances and essential oils, used for the treatment of diseases. This knowledge has been passed down to us on clay tablets inscribed in cuneiform with detailed lists of plant substances. Recipes did not mention the proportions, but special emphasis was placed on preparation and applications for the products.

The decoctions, which included plant substances, were prepared the night before. It was recommended that they be used just before sundown or at night. Out of more than two hundred and fifty plants used in Mesopotamian recipes, a large number were prescribed in Egypt, and later in Arabic medicine. In addition, five thousand-year-old terracotta pots used for extracted essences have been found at some archaeological sites, and confirm the importance of essential oils for these cultures.

Shell for cosmetics (circa 700-600 BCE). This type of shell, which in this case depicts a carving of a woman's face, was likely produced in the region that is now Syria and Palestine. It has been found in Mesopotamia and Egypt, even as far away as Greece.

Cuneiform cylinder. Babylon (circa 539-530 BCE). Recounting of the conquest of Babylon in 539 BCE by Cyrus, king of Persia.

The garden of the king of Babylon

The Babylonian king Marduk-apla-iddina II (722-710 BCE) had a garden in which more than sixty species of medicinal plants grew. These included thyme, saffron, mustard, dill, myrrh, roses, mandrake, poppy, henbane, boxwood, calamus, purslane, caraway, coriander, fennel, juniper, oleander, mustard, and licorice. Fruit trees such as apple and pomegranate, and plants such as garlic, onions, squash, and cucumbers were also cultivated.

China

Ancient Chinese medicine also used natural and herbal remedies for proper nutrition and in acupuncture. They form the basis for what today has come to be known as traditional Chinese medicine.

To date, the number of plants used in Chinese antiquity far exceeds those used by any other culture. In fact, modern medicine owes many of its ingredients to Chinese plants. For example, rhubarb, ephedrine, ginseng, and tea are commonly used. Interestingly, many of the medicinal plants used most frequently in China correspond to those used in Europe, and there is evidence that, even without the benefit of scientific analysis, they were equally effective. These include burdock, tarragon, gentians, rhubarb, castor, aconite, caraway, walnut, plantain, licorice, peach, pomegranate, and Chinese tea.

Classical Greece

In the fifth century BCE Herodotus, the famous Greek historian, transcribed a system of distillation of turpentine and recorded information about perfumes and aromatic substances.

Hippocrates, known as the "father of medicine," studied the Egyptian tradition and used all kinds of medicinal plants and drugs, among them narcotics such as opium, henbane, belladonna, and the well-known mandrake. Among the natu-

The Chinese treatise on pharmacology, the *Pen-tsao Kang-mu*, which was published around 1597, contains 8,160 formulas drawn from 1,871 substances, mainly derived from plants.

Did you know...?

● In ancient Greece it was strongly believed that aromatic baths were essential to a healthy and peaceful life, and that these essences had the ability to cure various ailments.

Fragment of a Greek drinking vessel with a depiction of an aromatic bath.

ral remedies he prescribed were ointments and perfumed vapors. In addition, he recommended aromatherapy baths and massage techniques and performed aromatic fumigations to rid Athens of the plague.

A theory of correspondences, which prevailed until the Middle Ages, came into being at that time. It argued that there was a relationship between the characteristics of a plant and the cure attributed to it. For example, leaves of the liverwort were prescribed to combat liver disease, the yellow rhizomes of rhubarb for jaundice, the flowers and berries of the pomegranate for bleeding, lungwort for pulmonary problems, etc.

Rome

Greek physicians were much in demand in Rome, where they had disciples and created schools. The Greek physician Dioscorides, personal physician to Claudius and Nero, studied medicinal plants of the Mediterranean basin and compiled his knowledge in five volumes entitled *De materia medica*. It is possible that he recommended that Nero use rose-oil to soothe headaches and chamomile to heal the skin, both popular remedies at the time.

Galen, the personal physician of the Emperor Marcus Aurelius, was inspired by Hippocrates and decisively influenced the next generations. He is credited with having had an extensive knowledge of the many medicinal plants with which he pre-

pared remedies. His studies led him to create the division into several groups of substances derived from plants and he founded the branch of medicine called "Galenic Formulation," which is a science devoted to the principles and development of medicinal preparations. Today, in fact, in honor of his name, the active ingredients in medications are known as "galenics."

After the fall of the Roman Empire, many physicians fled to Constantinople where they continued their work. Their works were kept in the library of Alexandria and were translated into Arabic, including that of the physician Dioscorides, which made a decisive impact on the world of Arab medicine.

Perfume vessel in the shape of a lion (340–300 BCE). Animal forms like these were popular during the Etruscan period.

Roman baths

Inspired by the Egyptians and Greeks, the Romans developed spas. These were public baths perfumed with plants, flowers, woods and resins held to be beneficial to health. However, the main objective was the enjoyment of the pleasure of these essences.

Arab medicine and Avicenna

Abū ʿAlī al-Ḥusayn ibn ʿAbd Allāh ibn Sīnā, known as Avicenna, was an extraordinary Arab physician, born in the year 980. He was barely twenty years old when he wrote his famous medical compendium, Canon of Medicine, considered as a seminal book in France well into the seventeenth century. Much ancient learning was preserved in the Arabic world to be rediscovered by Europeans in the late Middle Ages and early Renaissance.

The Arabic world's taste for essences derived from plants and flowers, especially attar of roses, is well-known.

Medieval Europe and the Renaissance

Medicinal plants necessarily formed the basis for many of the natural remedies that were used in the Middle Ages and that on numerous occasions were negatively associated with witchcraft. However, in the twelfth century aromatherapy was introduced, brought from the East by physicians during the Crusades, who working alongside Arabs, learned the importance of hygiene and oils. Upon returning to Europe they brought with them not only essential oils but also sufficient knowledge about how to obtain them through the technique of distillation.

In the following centuries, monastic orders were responsible for perpetuating and expanding the knowledge of herbal medicine. They cultivated medicinal plants and prepared herbal remedies.

In the fourteenth century pine incense was burned in the streets to combat the Black Death that swept through Europe. Something similar occurred in seventeenth-century England when lavender, cedar and cypress were used for the same purpose.

In the sixteenth century, the printing press contributed dramatically to the dissemination of knowledge on medicinal plants and their distillation, with works like Hieronymus Braunschweig's 1597 *Liber de arte distillandi simplicia et composite* (The Art of Simple and Compound Distillation).

Paracelsus (b. 1493) was a Swiss physician and alchemist who coined the term "quintessence" for the essential oils he used to create medicines derived from plants. However, the "darkness" that

Charlemagne

The wise Charlemagne commanded that all of the gardens in his kingdom should be cultivated with specific types of plants for therapeutic applications. Thus began the acclimatization of some plants that were hitherto almost unknown in Europe..

prevailed at that time led to his being punished and expelled from the profession for his ideas.

In the seventeenth century, the European population began to increase, and the sanitary conditions in cities worsened. It was then that essential oils became fundamental in kits used by doctors and herbalists. This century also gave rise to the profession of perfumery and also the perfume industry, which had previously been associated with the work of the apothecary.

The contemporary development of aromatherapy

During the nineteenth century scientific research began on the essential oils that are used today in aromatherapy. Later, during the First World War, René-Maurice Gattefossé used essential oils to heal soldiers' wounds. A few years later, Marguerite Maury studied essential oils in relation to cosmetics. Gradually, the interest in oils spread to Great Britain, which was more inclined to use them for cosmetics and massage, in contrast to the Gallic regions where the focus was on medicinal applications. Another key figure in modern aromatherapy was Dr. Jean Valnet, who applied his knowledge of aromatherapy during the wars in Southeast Asia and contributed to its dissemination in France. Also, Robert Tisserand became one of the most respected personalities in the world of essential oils, beginning in the 1970s, mainly in Britain. He was responsible for the development of extensive research and teaching, and founded the Tisserand Institute, which is the most prestigious training center in aromatherapy to date. In the 1990s, Pierre Franchomme and Daniel Pénoël unveiled their research on the chemistry and therapeutic applications of essential oils. This formed a scientific basis for the fundamental knowledge of the properties of each of the oils and has significantly augmented the research and knowledge of new treatments. There are still many things to discover, but applications for health and beauty described in the pages of this book are pleasant and effective and are based on long experience.

Gattefossé and aromatherapy

One day Gattefossé accidentally burned his hand in the laboratory, and instinctively reached for a receptacle that contained the essential oil of lavender. He was astonished to find that after a few hours the burn healed well, and there was no inflammation. He realized that what had been considered an essence for perfume could also have potent therapeutic effects. He then began the research that today is modern aromatherapy.

Essences and essential oils

Discover essential oils

As previously stated, essences are found inside plants and are the product of complex biochemical processes that occur in secretory glands. The aroma of the plant is also known as the "essence," and the liquid that results from the process of extracting the essence of the plant is the "essential oil." Let us turn to these methods of extraction.

In fact, the term "essence" is somewhat abstract because it encompasses a wide range, and is poorly defined. For example, any products obtained by a method of extraction are also termed "essences," irrespective of whether or not they have been distilled, or are synthetic products that imitate a natural aroma, or a natural and synthetic mix, marketed as pure essential oils at higher prices.

Without a doubt, if you want good results always look for pure essential oils of the highest quality, even though the price might seem a bit high. Extracting a particular essential oil requires a lot of high quality raw material, and the end result is not inexpensive. However, since only a few drops are required, a small flask should suffice for many massages and pleasant baths, so ultimately, using essential oils is not as expensive as it might seem at the time of purchase.

Each plant can produce one or more distinct

essential oils, depending on factors such as solar radiation. In other words, the lavender grown in France does not have the same properties as that which is cultivated in Spain. And sometimes plants from the same region grow in different terrain and hours of sunlight. Indeed, factors such as the prevalence and the number of hours the plant is exposed to the sun directly affect the chemical composition of the substance that is

produced, and it is therefore important to consider the chemotype, or predominant chemical composition, of an essential oil.

It is also important that you know from which part of the plant the essential oil has been extracted. Secretory glands are found in fruits, flowers, leaves, stems, roots, and seeds. In addition, certain essential oils are extracted from wood such as sandalwood, or from seeds such as angelica or celery. In some cases, such as that of the orange, up to three different types of essential oils can be extracted: orange from the peel, neroli or orange blossom from the flower, and petit grain from the leaf. The properties of each one are different, so you have to consider the source.

Chemical composition of essential oils

Despite what the name might suggest, essentials oils do not have a viscous consistency. On the contrary, they are usually liquid, and very rarely crystalize. One of their main characteristics, as opposed to plant oils or fatty acids, is that they are volatile, meaning that they evaporate easily. Many, such as rosemary and lavender, retain the consistency of water or alcohol. Others are viscous and sticky because they are

resins, such as myrrh, frankincense and vetiver, while the damask rose is semisolid at room temperature and liquid at the slightest rise in temperature. However, with the exception of resins, they are lighter than water although they do not dissolve in it. Appearing in a variety of many colors, they almost never correspond to the color of the plant from which they were extracted. Some essential oils can also stain clothing.

The chemical composition of essential oils can be complex, and this is what gives them therapeutic properties. Their chemical structures may contain over one hundred chemicals

What is a chemotype?

A chemotype is an "identity card" or "fingerprint" of the essence of each oil. Therein is described each and every one of the many chemical components that are present in the essence of a plant. This composition can vary greatly, not only within the same species but also within the same plant, as with thyme or rosemary. The variation reaches such extremes that a type of thyme can have some therapeutic characteristics while another has a different chemotype with altogether different characteristics. Therefore, it is important to check the chemotype when selecting an essential oil. The chemotype can be identified with the help of gas chromatography and spectrometry.

that are divided into categories generally classified as terpenes, esters, aldehydes, ketones, alcohols, phenols, and oxides. This explains why a single essential oil has such a wide range of therapeutic properties. It should be noted that alcohols and esters usually have gentle healing properties and can be used at home without any type of risk. In contrast, ketones, aldehydes, and phenols should be left in hands of professionals, as their therapeutic properties are much more powerful, and irresponsible use can lead to discomfort. In fact, oils containing very high concentrations of these chemicals are rarely used in aromatherapy, and then only in

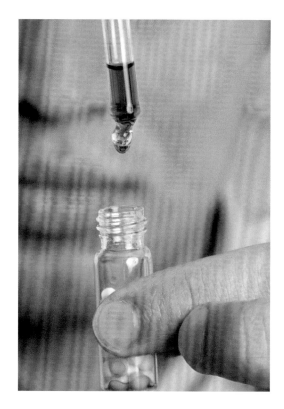

Organic essential oils

Essential oils are natural because they are derived from plants, but it is also important that they be organic. Today there are companies that only produce essential oils from organic plants, and it is these that offer the greatest guarantees. As we have seen, the chemotype is very important and varies depending on the region, soil, and other external factors that directly influence the plant. Modern life has introduced unnatural factors such as fertilizers and pesticides that have a major impact on the chemotype.

Although these chemicals increase the yield of medicinal plants, they might also remain in the mixture obtained at the end of the extraction process, and alter the desired effect on the person receiving a massage or bath.

very small doses for quick-relief of a specific problem.

It seems that a large number of chemical products that contain oil reach a natural and perfect balance that prevents, as a general rule, side effects from developing. They are manufactured to be accurately reproduced in the laboratory. This balance and synergy between the chemical elements that constitute essential oils also affect the level of toxicity, because it offsets other components and neutralizes them.

It is therefore crucial that you use pure and natural essential oils, as these are the only ones that retain all of the components and in the right amount, meaning that they contain all of their properties and benefits. In addition, they possess what practitioners call "life breath" or "life force," originating from their source and natural balance.

A gas chromatograph separates the main components of essential oils by monitoring the "chemical fingerprint" produced by each one. However, the structure of the substance in its natural state is very complex, and it is not possible to obtain an exact replica of the aroma by mixing different chemical components in a laboratory. Nevertheless, we will describe some of the major components found in essential oils and their major therapeutic effects.

The energy of aromas

 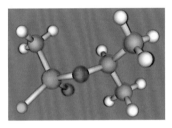

The French researchers Pénoël and Franchomme argued that the electric charge of aromatic molecules is a fundamental aspect of the therapeutic property of essential oils. Their studies have shown that molecules either gain or lose electrons. Accordingly, the molecules that lose electrons, called "anions" cause a "negativante" effect, which results in relaxing and soothing properties. In contrast, molecules that gain electrons, or "cations", are "positivantes" and possess invigorating and stimulating properties. Aldehydes, ketones, esters, and sesquiterpenes are examples of anions. The most commonly known cations are: acid, coumarins, lactones, aromatic aldehydes, phenols, alcohol, oxides, phenol methyl ether, and terpenes. This would explain why, from the point of view of energy, some essential oils are relaxing and others are stimulants. The best examples of this are lavender and rosemary, respectively. However, there are a few essential oils that have the capability to "normalize." Hyssop helps to raise low blood pressure or lower high blood pressure. In the same way, bergamot and geranium can sedate or stimulate according to personal needs.

ACIDS

Anti-inflammatory properties are found in small quantities and combined with alcohols form esters (geranic acid, campholenic acid).

ALCOHOLS

Molecules endowed with good disinfectant properties, but are less potent than phenols.
Examples: alpha-terpineol, citronellol, geraniol, linalol, menthol, nerol, 4-terpineol, tuyanol.

ALDEHYDES

These are very common and are potent anti-inflammatories.
Examples: citrals (geranial, neral, citroneral, cuminaldehyde).

CUMARINS

These have a small presence in essential oils, but their sedative and anticoagulant capacity is very powerful, as in the case of dicumarol. Furanocoumarins (bergapten) cause photosensitivity, so the essential oils containing them, such as bergamot and citrus, should generally not be applied before sunbathing.

ESTERS

These usually have a subtle antispasmodic effect. They are aromatic molecules resulting from the combination of an acid and an alcohol (acetate, benzoate, butyrate, formate, propionate).

ETHERS

Molecules composed of a phenolic nucleus and a

functional group (methyl). Some ethers are powerful antispasmodics. These are atenolol (anise, badiana, fennel) and estragole (basil, tarragon).

KETONES

These have important mucolytic and healing properties, but should be used with care and prescribed by a specialist due to neurotoxicity.
Examples: camphor, carvone, krypton, fenchone, menthone, pulegone, thujone.

LACTONES

This is an extensive class of chemicals with excellent mucolytic and expectorant properties. However, it should only be used under the supervision of a specialist because it can irritate the skin.

OXIDES

Aromatic molecules containing an atom of oxygen. The most common is 1.8 cineol (eucalyptol), recognized for its effect on the respiratory tract.

PHENOLS

From the family of aromatics, known to be disinfectants and stimulants of the central nervous system. It includes, among others, australol, carvacrol, eugenol and thymol. The oils that they contain can be very irritating, so they should only be used under supervision of a specialist.

TERPENES

Molecules comprised solely of carbon or hydrogen atoms. The most commonly known are pinene (conifers), limonene (citrus) and phellandrene. They contain energizing properties at a physical level, and if sprayed in the environment are potent antibacterial agents and antiseptics.

Volatility

All essential oils have a common characteristic: volatility. This means that their aromatic source easily evaporates if left exposed to sunlight or if not kept hermetically sealed. This characteristic is the main difference between fixed oils or lipids, such as almond or wheat germ, and those used in aromatherapy as carrier oils.

However, not all essential oils have the same volatility. In fact, the smaller the molecules, the faster they evaporate. Correspondingly, the larger the molecules are, the heavier and less volatile the essential oil is.

The quality of an essential oil can be measured by its volatility. The better the quality of the essential oil, the higher the volatility. And the reason for this is very simple. Synthetic essential oils always retain their aroma, which is usually penetrating and uniform, precisely because they are not exclusively composed of natural ingredients.

In contrast, natural essential oils evaporate easily. Thus, for proper preservation, they must be stored in dark glass bottles and protected from light in order to conserve their therapeutic properties and fragrance.

And it is the perfume that can be therapeutic and also help us with our emotions, thought processes, memory, learning ability and, of course, sexual responses. The type of perfume that each one offers is therefore a new means of classifying essential oils. Connoisseurs of fragrance classify them using the same terms as for music, namely, with high notes, middle notes, and base notes. Thus, if an oil is composed of small molecules, or highly volatile, it is said that these form the high notes of the scent, the first one to reach our sense of smell. Next we capture the middle notes, and finally, the base notes, which are the last to evaporate and to reach our nostrils. As previously stated, the high notes or output of an essential oil evaporate quickly and maintain their scent for a short time, approximately one hour.

Volatility is mainly due to the components of green aromatic citrus fruits and white flowers, which result in a cool and ethereal scent. These include bergamot, lavender, coriander and lemon. These form part of the group of essentials oils that are the most readily perceived on account of their fresh aromas, citric and clear.

The middle note, which also has the poetic name "heart," comprises essential oils with warmer fragrances that give fullness to the blend and in addition, last a little longer. If these are blended with fragrances of the high note, they will only emerge once the more volatile fragrance has dissipated, after an hour or so, and it will be two to three hours more before they disappear.

They are the central part of the fragrance, provided by aldehydes, fruits, flowers and spices. Ylang ylang, clary sage, and rose are some of the most popular "heart" oils. Their sweet aromas, fragrant and pleasant, provide volume, richness and exoticism.

Finally, the bass note is the most tenacious and corresponds to the heaviest aromas that linger on our skin and help to bind the essences or essential oils that form a fragrance or a preparation of oils. Its aroma arises after three or four hours and can remain on your skin for more than a day.

These base notes are fundamentally woody, oriental, amber, and musky like patchouli, sandalwood, and vetiver. Their aroma is deep, sweet, and penetrating, lending persistence and character to the fragrance.

The table on the next page provides an extensive overview of the volatility of essential oils. Some are halfway between one note and another and can help you balance a blend.

Active principles and therapeutic properties

The active principles of plants remain unchanged when converted to essential oils and provide us with all of their therapeutic benefits when they penetrate our body.

Many of these active ingredients have been successfully synthesized in laboratories and form the basis of many prescribed medications.

As we have seen, the effect of aromatherapy is beneficial, except in some specific cases, and our body and mind react positively to its therapeutic effect. Furthermore, this effect can manifest in many different ways, which we will describe in the table on the following page. We have grouped the major physiological effects into categories, in the same way as is done with drugs, and we provide a brief sketch of the essential oils that can help you when your mind or your body is in need of treatment.

Volatility of essential oils

High / NOTE — ESSENTIAL OIL
- Angelica
- Basil
- Bergamot
- Cardamom
- Eucalyptus
- Fennel
- Grapefruit
- Lavender
- Mandarin
- Mint
- Orange
- Petitgrain

Middle-High / NOTE — ESSENTIAL OIL
- Black Pepper
- Chamomile
- Clary Sage
- Damascene Rose
- Geranium
- Ginger, Grapefruit
- Lavender, Mint
- Neroli
- Palmarossa
- Orange
- Petitgrain
- Pine Needle
- Rose Absolute

Middle-Bass — ESSENTIAL OIL
- Cypress
- Jasmine
- Myrrh
- Orange Blossom Absolute
- Rose, Vanilla
- Ylang Ylang

Bass-middle / NOTE
- Cedar
- Frankincense
- Jasmine
- Myrrh
- Sandalwood

Bass / NOTE — ESSENTIAL OIL
- Cedar
- Frankincese
- Patchouli
- Sandalwod
- Vetiver

High-Middle / NOTE
- Angelica
- Basil
- Bergamot
- Cardamom
- Fennel
- Geranium
- Lavender
- Neroli
- Petitgrain

Middle / NOTE
- Black Pepper
- Chamomile
- Cinnamon Stick (for ambience)
- Clary Sage
- Clove (for ambience)
- Damascene Rose
- Geranium
- Ginger, Grapefruit
- Lavender, Marjoram
- Neroli, Palmarossa
- Orange Blossom Absolute
- Rose Absolute
- Vanilla
- Ylang Ylang

Therapeutic properties of essential oils

Therapeutic Property	Description	Essential Oils
Analgesics	Sooth or alleviate pain	Tea Tree, Bergamot, Cajuput, Lavender, Chamomile, Peppermint, Rosemary
Antidepressants	Help to overcome depression	Basil, Bergamot, Geranium, Jasmine, Lavender, Chamomile, Lemon Balm, Orange, Neroli, Patchouli, Rose, Clary Sage, Sandalwood, Ylang Ylang
Anti-inflammatory	Reduces inflammation	Cajuput, Lavender, Chamomile, Peppermint, Rose
Antispasmodics	Calms and alleviates muscle spasms	Cajuput, Eucalyptus, Juniper, Fennel, Sage, Chamomile, Marjoram, Sweet Orange, Black Pepper, Rosemary, Rose, Lavender
Antiseptics	Although almost all of the essential oils have a property that kills germs, there are some that have a much more powerful antiseptic capacity.	Tea Tree, Bergamot, Juniper, Eucalyptus, Lavender, Lemon, Sweet Orange, Pine, Rosemary, Sandalwood, Thyme
Aphrodisiacs	Sexual stimulation is attributed to these	Fennel, Jasmine, Neroli, Patchouli, Rosemary, Rose, Clary Sage, Sandalwood, Ylang Ylang
Astringents	Reduce the flow of bodily fluids and contract the tissues	Cedar, Cypress, Geranium, Frankincense, Lemon, Myrrh, Patchouli, Rose, Clary Sage, Sandalwood
Carminatives	Soothe or alleviate flatulence and bloating	Cardamom, Clove, Fennel, Ginger, Chamomile, Mint
Cautery	Promotes the formation of new tissues	Frankincense, Lavender, Neroli, Rose, Sandalwood
Deodorants	Neutralize body odor and give a fresh fragrance	Tea Tree, Cypress, Lemongrass, Eucalyptus, Lavender, Rosemary
Diuretics	Facilitate the elimination of fluids through the urine	Cedar, Cypress, Juniper, Geranium, Fennel, Lavender, Lemon, Bergamot, Grapefruit, Clary Sage

Therapeutic Property	Description	Essential Oils
Emmenagogues	Provoke and stimulate menstrual flow	Basil, Fennel, Hyssop, Lavender, Lemon, Chamomile, Clary Sage, Sandalwood
Fungicides	Combat the development of microscopic fungi	Tea Tree
Hepatics	Improve hepatic functions	Cardamom, Lemon, Chamomile, Peppermint, Rose
Hypertensives	Help to elevate low blood pressure	Rosemary
Hypotensives	Help to lower high blood pressure	Geranium, Lavender, Lemon, Melissa, Ylang Ylang
Invigorators	Invigorate the body or a specific area	Basil, Cardamom, Juniper, Geranium, Fennel, Hyssop, Frankincense, Jasmine, Lavender, Chamomile, Marjoram, Melissa, Myrrh, Patchouli, Black Pepper, Rose, Clary Sage, Sandalwood
Nervines	Promote balance in nervous disorders	Basil, Bergamot, Cypress, Geranium, Jasmine, Laurel, Lavender, Lemon, Mandarin, Chamomile, Marjoram, Melissa, Mint, Orange, Neroli, Patchouli, Rose, Clary Sage, Sandalwood
Rubefacients	Help to increase peripheral blood flow	Cajuput, Coriander, Juniper, Eucalyptus, Ginger, Black Pepper, Rosemary
Sedatives	Help to reduce stress and alleviate nervous disorders	Chamomile, Marjoram, Myrrh, Neroli, Sage, Sandalwood, Ylang Ylang
Stimulants	Help to stimulate physical and intellectual performance	Physical: Geranium, Black Pepper, Rosemary, Rose, Thyme Mental: Basil, Tea Tree, Eucalyptus, Lemon, Mint, Thyme.
Vasoconstrictors	Constrict capillaries and veins	Camphor, Cypress, Chamomile, Mint
Vermífuges	Help expel intestinal worms	Camphor, Bergamot, Eucalyptus, Hyssop, Lavander, Melissa, Mint.
Vulneraries	Promote the healing of cuts, sores and wounds	Camphor, Benzoin, Bergamot, Juniper, Eucalyptus, Geranium, Hyssop, Frankincense, Lavender, Chamomile, Myrrh, Rosemary

Methods of extraction

There are several extraction methods. These vary according to which part of the plant is used to obtain the essential oil, and also the desired quality and therapeutic value of the extracted material. Each of the extraction method yields a different product - if the plant provides more than one - because extractions from each part of the plant are composed of several components. What they indeed all have in common is that the method is laborious and lengthy because, depending on the location, the aromatic principles need to be released slowly. Also, in order to obtain a minimum amount of essential oil, large amounts of raw materials are always required. For example, one kilo of lavender essential oil requires as much as two hundred kilos of fresh lavender flowers.

If instead of lavender, we wish to obtain rose essential oil, between two and five tons of rose petals are required for the kilo of essential oil. And if you prefer lemon, no less than three thousand are required in the extraction process. These examples also help us to understand why it may seem that essential oils are expensive. And we say "seem" because in reality they are not. A little goes a long way.

Steam distillation

This is without doubt the most commonly used method for obtaining pure essential oils. It has thousands of years of history and is still practiced today, although with the most modern equipment. In antiquity, the Egyptians placed raw materials and water in large clay pots that were subjected to heat. The water vapor then passed through several layers of linen or cotton that covered the mouth of the vessel. Finally they wrung out the fabric, which released the precious drops of essential oil. Later, Avicenna invented the alembic, and since then although the technique has been improved upon, basically it remains the same.

Not all plants can be distilled. Distillation requires very high temperatures. and these cannot be sustained by all varieties. It is used primarily in the *Labiatae* genus, such as mint. It cannot be applied to flower petals, the chemical components of which cannot sustain these temperatures. In this case essences are extracted from essential oil glands found in the leaves.

The method consists of using an alembic to distill plant cuttings. Once the pieces of leaves are fully compressed inside the alembic, they are subjected to the direct action of the water vapor. For this reason, this process is also known as the "pull

Three images from the film Perfume: the Story of a Murderer, directed by Tom Tykwer. Based on a novel of the same title by the German author Patrick Suskind, it is set in eighteenth-century France. It tells the story of a young man who has an uncanny ability to capture scents. He enters the workshop of a prestigious perfumery and devotes his life to obtaining the ultimate scent, and in the process, does not hesitate to sacrifice human lives. A beautiful and lyrical hyperbole of a passion for perfumes elevated to madness.

extraction method." High temperatures cause the essence-filled glands to burst, evaporate, and mix with the steam. The steam is then conducted towards a coil that cools the steam and converts it into a liquid. The result is a composite liquid composed of essential oil and hydrosol, the watery distillate that has separated from the essential oil. In general, essential oils are lighter than water, and can therefore be easily extracted. However, there are a few cases where the essential oil is heavier than water, such as mandarin, and density is used for the separation system.

The steam distillation method of extraction results in a liquid that is water based. The liquid is then decanted into a Florence flask, where the hydrosols are separated out, and the essential oil is extracted.

Hydrosols are not utilized as much as the essential oil, although they contain valuable water-soluble plant substances as well as other liposolubles, which are dissolved in water and fat. These byproducts have very interesting applications, especially in cosmetics and confectionery. Rosewater, lemon balm, witch hazel and orange blossom are among the best-known hydrosols. These are used to market lines of natural cosmetics, although generally the "waters" of roses and orange blossoms found in shops are composed of water-soluble synthetic essences, and obviously do not have the beneficial properties of the plants.

It is therefore essential that you buy quality, natural products.

Expression

Expression, also known as "crushing," is the ultimate system for the extraction of essential oils from citrus peels, which contain a large quantity of essences. The most commonly known are lemon, lime, orange, mandarin, grapefruit, and bergamot. At first a manual process was employed in which the essence was collected with sponges during a long and laborious process. In modern times centrifugal force is used in an industrial process to extract both the juice and the essence.

The product extracted by means of this system has a shorter shelf-life than the one extracted by distillation. It is not an essential oil, because the substance obtained from the citrus peel has not undergone any alteration. It is an essence that has not been subject to either heat or distillation and can be of two types: volatile and non-volatile. However, in the other extraction methods only volatile substances can be obtained, meaning that they have the ability to evaporate or dissolve and,

therefore, are essential oils.

Extraction by volatile solvents

This is currently the most widely used system and involves passing hot volatile solvents through plants in order to dissolve their aromatic substances into liquid. Once saturated with essences, the solvents evaporate and the natural principle is isolated. The drawback of this method is that it is impossible to completely eliminate the chemical residue of the solvent from the essential oils. These are usually toxic and dangerous. Hexane and ether of petroleum are the ones most commonly used today. As it is impossible to avoid minimal traces of these solvents remaining in the product, it is important that these essential oils never be taken internally.

This method is most widely used in perfumery because it is cost effective and not used for therapeutic products. On the other hand, essential oils used in aromatherapy should be obtained by distillation rather than by extraction with volatile solvents.

The essential oil obtained by this process is called "concrete." This product contains all of the aromatic substances, pigments, and waxes which can be extracted from any plant and has a waxy consistency, but it does not have the

Damascene roses grow, among other places, in the valley of M'Gouna in Morocco. Farmers sell them by the dozen to make rose water and essential oils.

right balance of chemical components that would enable it to be used in therapy. When used for plants and resins, the product is called "resinoid."

This method is used for those plants that cannot sustain heat, such as flowers, and has completely replaced the classic system which used to be used for the same purpose: cold enfleurage. Jasmine is the concrete most characteristic of this method of extraction.

Enfleurage

This name is applied to the classical method par excellence for the extraction of the aromatic source and is used by perfumers and makers of cosmetics. It was used only with flowers, the structure of which cannot be subjected to the high temperatures of the steam distillation method. The most expensive perfumes were ob-

tained by this method.

In hot enfleurage flowers are arranged in thin layers on trays, smeared with odorless fat, under the gentle warmth of the sun or in a double boiler for the length of time necessary to absorb the essence. Afterwards, the fat is filtered through cotton or linen cloth, to obtain an ointment or perfumed oil, and then washed with pure alcohol for a fat-free liquid extract.

Fat is also used in cold enfleurage, usually pork fat, but it is not subjected to the effect of heat. Instead it is permeated as many times as necessary to be saturated with essence. Next, the product is treated with cold alcohol to extract the essence of the fat, known as the absolute. This laborious process is rarely used today, since extraction by solvents gives the same results, but it was the quintessential method in Provence, the Western cradle of perfume.

Dilution

From a concrete, an absolute can be extracted. In this method, the concrete is washed with strong alcohol in which some elements dissolve. After the concrete is allowed to evaporate the absolute is obtained. It has a different chemical composition and some other purposes too. This method is used to treat resinoids, such as tree gums and resins such as myrrh, frankincense and galbanum.

To extract these from trees, exudation is caused by a blow or a small cut in the trunk, then treated to obtain the absolutes.

We cannot avoid mentioning that resins containing these alcohol resinoids have a chemical structure similar to human steroids, or male and female hormones, and directly affect their stimulation.

Supercritical CO2 Extraction

This modern method passes a stream of CO_2 through a plant mass that has been captured from the atmosphere and converted into liquid. The aggregate is subjected to a pressure of 73.80 bars and 31 ° C, conditions that achieve the supercritical CO_2 state and convert into an effective solvent with the chemical components of the plant mass. Since high temperatures are not used, the result is brightly colored, shiny and aromatic, very faithful to the plant as it was before

being subjected to the process of extraction. One of the great advantages of this method is that it does not generate pollutants, while capturing the original essence.

Macerated oils

Macerated oils are produced by a similar system, though it is not as laborious and does not have the same chemical properties. This method involves macerating oil or fatty substances by heating plants. It does not produce essential oils nor essences, rather a macerated oil or oily ex-

The modern methods for producing essential oils combine theoretical principles of "classic" aromatherapy with more advanced machinery, as shown in the image on the left.

tract that has some properties of plants that have been infused, such as hypericum, calendula and arnica. However, macerated oils are beneficial, and also serve as fine carrier oils when added to essential oils.

Antibacterial properties of aromas

It is a fully documented fact that in ancient times, perfumers were often immune to the plague. This led to the development of the infamous Vinegar of the Four Thieves (a blend of garlic and aromatic plant essences suspended in vinegar), which was named after four thieves who, during the Great Plague of Marseille in 1722, merrily sprinkled themselves with it before looting the corpses of plague victims. The four lived to tell the tale and loot again with impunity.

After they were arrested, they were saved from condemnation by revealing the secret of their miracle-formula to the authorities. The mayor mandated that placards with the formula be posted on all the walls of the city so that the inhabitants could make the miraculous vinegar at home. Apparently this vinegar had the ability to repel insects, which were the main transmitters of the dreaded plague in the first half of the eighteenth century.

Plant oils: carriers of essences

Essential oils have cosmetic and therapeutic properties, but in most cases cannot be applied directly to the skin. Only a very small amount is needed, and the best way to absorb all of their benefits through our skin is by adding them to massage oil. Massage oils come from a vegetal source and do not evaporate. They belong to a biochemical group that is distinct from that of essential oils. In terms of chemistry, these constitute lipids, and in nature are found in different types of oily plants and seeds.

In aromatherapy this oil is called "carrier oil" or "base." Its real function is this: it carries infinitesimal parts of valuable essential oils to every pore of our skin. Its lubricating quality facilitates massage movements and proper distribution.

However, carrier oils also affect our health by their own characteristics, and different

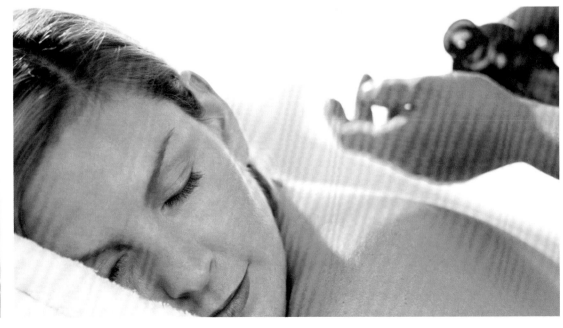

types are used to contribute to the physico-chemical and therapeutic properties of the desired end result. The ones selected can have regenerative properties, acting as emollients, antioxidants and also as a source of vitamins. Once again, aromatherapy harnesses the benefits offered by nature and provides us with wellbeing by virtue of essential oils and base oils.

In fact, any plant oil that has no perfume can be considered a base oil. But it has to be expressed by a cold process in order to maintain all its properties and remain free of toxic elements as the by-product of refining, which would not be the case with solvents or expression at high temperatures. The term is not entirely accurate, because the process itself causes an increase in temperature, but this is always below 60 degrees Celsius. Once obtained, it is left to cool. It then has practically the same characteristics as natural oils, that is to say, virgin oils.

If these prerequisites are met, we may safely use olive, soybean and sunflower oil. However, these oils are very dense and can result in tough stains on clothing that are difficult to remove. On account of this, sweet almond, grape seed, and sesame are normally used.

Each has its own specific properties and applications, and it is important to note the base oil used in each case, so that it can enrich the therapeutic properties of massage with its own benefits.

Bear in mind that these are natural products and can become rancid quite easily. To avoid this, you must buy them in small quantities and keep them in suitable containers, protected from light and heat. Refined oils, made by a more elaborate process, have a longer life, but lack the benefits of virgin oils. So one should always use unrefined plant oils of a cold first pressing.

Furthermore, it is highly recommended to obtain organic oils that have been inspected and do not show traces of pesticides, fungicides, or fertilizers in their composition.

There is a wide range from which to choose. The criterion might be based on therapeutic properties, cosmetics, or simply texture. Below we describe those that are most commonly used.

MOST COMMONLY USED CARRIER OILS

AVOCADO

Avocado oil is characterized by its odor and green tone. It is not used alone, but as part of a mix, usually at a maximum of 10%. Is a viscous oil that nourishes the skin with fatty acids, protein and vitamins B, C and E. Readily absorbed, it reaches the deep layers of the epidermis. Furthermore, it is very useful in summer, because it protects against the sun's harmful rays. Cosmetic applications include treating dehydrated or mature skin, which responds very well to facial massage with a preparation containing avocado oil. Is also very suitable for eczema, skin that is flaking or cracked, and for preventing stretch marks.

APRICOT KERNEL SEED

This oil has a light texture and an extraordinary capacity for penetration. It is extracted from seeds of apricot (*Prunus armeniaca*) and is rich in vitamins, especially A, and minerals. In terms of properties, it is very moisturizing, making it ideal for treating sensitive or dry skin. It is used in cosmetics to relieve and treat dehydrated, sensitive or mature skin. From the therapeutic standpoint, it benefits inflamed or dry skin.

GRAPE SEED

This oil is very pure and odorless. It leaves intact the aroma of essential oils. In addition, its light texture does not leave the skin oily. It is most often used for body massages, as it is very light, penetrating and allows one to get dressed after the session without fear of staining clothing. Its high content of polyunsaturated fats stimulates collagen and elastin. These antioxidants help neutralize the free radicals that cause the cells to age. Since it is slightly astringent, it is very suitable for the treatment of young and acne-prone skin.con tendencia acnéica.

HAZELNUT

The texture of this oil is very liquid and light. It does not leave a greasy residue on the skin, and can be applied several times a day. It works well for eczema and dermatitis, and also sports massage and tonics. On account of its texture, it can be recommended for treating oily skin.

JOJOBA

This oil is obtained from a desert plant (*Simmondsia chinensis*) and its texture is reminiscent of the natural liquid wax that is typically used to thicken creams. In fact, its chemical composition is similar to the oil secreted by our sebaceous glands. Since it is very rich in vitamin E, it does not become rancid and helps to preserve other oils. A small amount is usually added to mixtures to prolong effectiveness. On account of its almost dry texture, it is not recommended for body massages, but it gives good results in face creams. It is typically used to treat the skin because it is not greasy and is easily absorbed. It has soothing and nourishing properties, and above all antioxidants, which help to slow the aging process of cells. It also protects against radiation, whether solar or from a computer, for example. Finally, note that it has antibacterial properties and is useful in the treatment of acne-prone skin.

ROSE MOSQUETA

It is extracted from the seeds of the fruit of a shrub belonging to the rose family

(*Rosaceae Rubiginosa linee*) that grows wild in rainy and cold climates. Today it is also cultivated for the extraction of its oil. The stems and branches are covered with thorns, and in ancient times it was a very popular shrub for making fences used in armed conflicts and land disputes. This precious oil has wonderful properties, and contains up to 80% of polyunsaturated fatty acids that help regenerate cells and revitalize the skin. In addition, it has a high vitamin content, particularly vitamins A, E, C, B1 and B2, plus antioxidants like flavonoids, pectin, riboflavin and polyphenols, which help fight the aging process of cutaneous cells. Therefore, it is efficacious in the treatment of burns, diaper rash, and for treating irritated skin. It is also reduces cutaneous spots and scars. It is used to combat wrinkles, for tired or mature skin, and the effects of exposure to the sun, wind, and cold. Oily or acne-prone skin is the only type of skin that does not work well with rose mosqueta oil, due to the high lipid content of this carrier. Because it provides great elasticity, it helps prevent the appearance of stretch marks on the skin during pregnancy or in people who experience constant fluctuations in body weight. It is therefore a carrier oil that is good for the body.

SWEET ALMOND

This is one of the most commonly used on account of its creamy texture. This makes it very suitable for massage because it has little absorption and so one application can last for an entire session. This feature also makes it an excellent skin protector, ideal for babies and any type of epidermis. It is obtained from the seed of a tree that grows in southern Europe (*Prunus amygdalus or dulcis*). In the market it is difficult to find organic sweet almond oil that is cold-pressed and pure, as it is often adulterated with sunflower oil. It is pale yellow with a mild flavor and odor. Of medium viscosity, it contains a large proportion of monounsaturated and polyunsaturated acids. It also has vitamins B1 and B6, and a small amount of vitamin E, which protects it from rancidity. Its main therapeutic application is as a antispasmodic. It also calms and soothes. It can therefore be used to treat eczema (such as diaper rash), stings, itches and any other type of irritation.

SESAME

Its viscous texture prevents it from being a good base oil, but it enriches mixtures of other plant and essential oils because it has vitamin E, a powerful antioxidant that helps preserve the mixture and combats the effects of aging skin and other skin disorders. In addition, on account of its anti-inflammatory property, it is highly recommended for rheumatism.

WHEAT GERM

Dark in color and with a pungent odor, it is viscous and not a good lubricant. However, it is a great source of vitamin E, so it nourishes and revitalizes the skin. It is not used as a carrier oil, but instead is added at a dilution of 10% in order to increase the shelf life of the mixture of the base oil and other essential oils. This will provide a massage oil that can last for six months instead of a few weeks. It is important to note that it cannot be used by people who are allergic to wheat, because it can cause reactions such as inflammation or irritation.

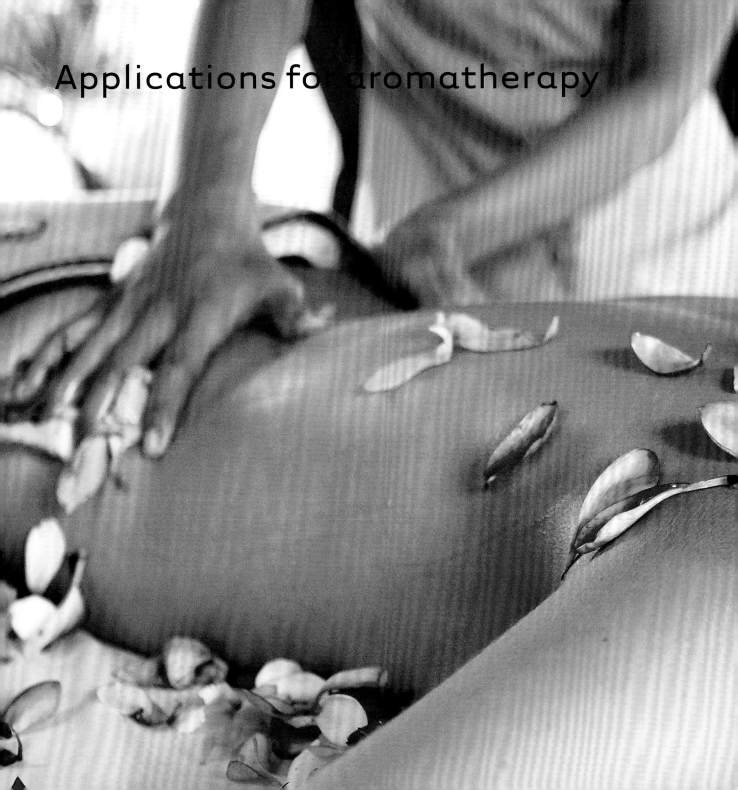

Applications for aromatherapy

Basic precautions for the use of essential oils

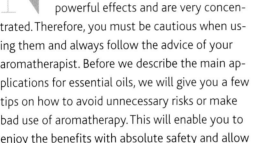

Natural does not mean harmless. Products that come from plants have very powerful effects and are very concentrated. Therefore, you must be cautious when using them and always follow the advice of your aromatherapist. Before we describe the main applications for essential oils, we will give you a few tips on how to avoid unnecessary risks or make bad use of aromatherapy. This will enable you to enjoy the benefits with absolute safety and allow essential oils to play an important role in maintaining your physical and emotional wellbeing.

Phototoxicity

There are certain essential oils, especially citrus essences, which should not be used shortly before exposure to the sun or while sunbathing. The reason is that they are phototoxic, and cause sunspots on skin that has been treated with certain active principles and has been exposed to ultraviolet rays. Sweet orange, bitter orange, bergamot and lemon are among the best known, but there are more. In the following chapter, we provide a list that indicates each case, so that you can take this into account when using them.

Skin irritation

All skin is different and special precautions should be taken when using more potent essential oils. However, if testing on a small area on the skin reaction does not cause a reaction, they can be safely used in moderation. Spicy essential oils often cause irritability, but lowering the dose is all that is needed to take advantage of their important benefits.

Drowsiness

Some essential oils contain powerful active ingredients with soothing, narcotic, hypnotic or sedative properties. They are ideal for a bath or massage before bed, or putting them in an essence-burner in your bedroom. They should be avoided, however, when working with machinery or driving, as they can cause drowsiness and make you take unnecessary risks. This characteristic will be discussed in further detail in the list of essential oils that we recommend in the next chapter.

Children and babies

As you know, the skin is one of the main ways through which the active ingredients of essential oils penetrate our body. Only certain essential oils should be used for babies and young children, and these should always be very diluted. At most, you should use only half the dose typical for adult skin. The skin of the little ones is extremely sensitive and you must only use the gentlest oils.

Diffusors and putting a few drops on your child's pillow are good options, and very safe. Adding essential oils to the bath is also safe, but use only a few drops and make sure that no water splashes into the eyes.

Pregnancy

One of the main things you should keep in mind is that most essential oils have therapeutic effects on the female hormonal and reproductive systems, namely the ovaries and the uterus. Thus, the characteristic that makes them beneficial for menstrual disorders, menopause or premenstrual syndrome, also places them on the "prohibited" list if you are pregnant.

Any attempt by your body to regulate menstruation and the hormonal system could lead to a miscarriage, so if you are pregnant we recommend that you use the utmost caution in deciding on aromatherapy.

On the list of the most common essential oils we indicate their tolerance in pregnant women, so you can choose what is safe with peace of mind.

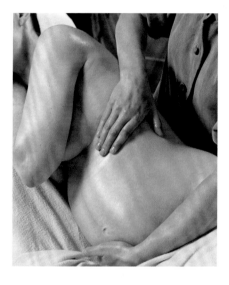

Asthma

Although it might appear that the balsamic oils are an ideal remedy for asthma, precautions should be taken so as to avoid inducing bronchial spasms. This could happen if you take steam inhalations, as we describe in the section that deals with asthma and its treatment in the next chapter.

Epilepsy and brain lesions

There are certain active principles in some essential oils that make them undesirable for the treatment of people who either suffer from epilepsy or have it in their family history. They are also not recommended for those who suffer from brain lesions.

Other recommendations

Aside from certain exceptions, such as lavender or tea tree, you should not apply essential oils directly to the skin. It is always best to dilute them in water or in a carrier oil to prevent skin reactions due to their high concentration and potent active ingredients.

● **Avoid prolonged use,** such as daily for two months, of the same essential oil, because your skin might become sensitized to that particular essential oil. It is better to put it aside and alternate or substitute it with another one that has the same or similar therapeutic properties. After a reasonable time you can safely return to it without risk.

● **People with a history of allergies** should use aromatherapy with a lot of caution. They should test a small area to eliminate the possibility of any reaction.

● **When you put essential oils in the bath,** stir the water well so that they are mixed in well and do not make direct contact with your skin.

● **Always avoid essential oils,** pure or diluted, coming into contact with your eyes as they may cause considerable irritation. If this occurs, try to

remain calm and do the following: rinse them immediately with a lot of water. Then use a few drops of sweet almond oil to dilute any small traces of essential oil that may have been left inside and, moreover, to soothe the irritation.

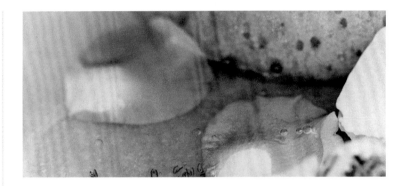

prescribed by a specialist.

● **If you are undergoing a homeopathic treatment,** you should not use peppermint or eucalyptus essential oil because the menthol they contain neutralizes the effects of the remedies prescribed by your homeopath.

● **Do not apply essential oils to a light bulb.** It is much better to put it on the hoops for sale in specialty shops, and place it on the bulb that way.

If you put essential oils on a burner, be sure to place it on a fireproof surface and do not leave it unattended.

●**You should never ingest any essential oil** unless a professional aromatherapist whom you trust completely has specifically prescribed it. This is of the utmost importance: do not ingest any essential oil on your own initiative except if

How to use essential oils

In the consultation room of a professional aromatherapist you can receive different treatments, usually in the form of massage. But in your own home you can continue to enjoy the benefits of this wonderful therapy through different applications, so you can continue to dedicate yourself to your own wellbeing, but in a more comfortable manner using essence burners, scented candles, aromatic baths, inhalations, restorative massages, hot or cold compresses... As you see, there is a wide range. We are going to describe these various applications, so that you may choose the most suitable for each occasion, and promote treatment at home for you and your family.

You should not have any qualms about resorting to aromatherapy. Its therapeutic benefits include what is good for our skin and complexion. A cosmetic treatment can improve the health of your skin, the largest organ of the entire body. You can also choose aromatherapy to combat cellulite, delay aging, and thoroughly nourish your skin after a day in the sun.

Therapeutic massage, cosmetics, aerial diffusion of relaxing essential oils, aphro-disiacs, all can create a cleansed atmosphere full of "good vibes." The perfume of essential oil will make you feel better, t freshen your home and closets, and make your home warm, calm, and fragrant.

In the following section we will explain the most common applications of essential oils so you can choose how to get started in aromatherapy, or simply understand the treatment that you are applying as prescribed by your aromatherapist or beautician.

Vaporization

The active ingredients in essential oils are extremely volatile and can reach your brain through your nose in a matter of seconds. One of the most common means of application is to put a few drops of one or more essential oils in a diffusor. It's easy and can be used in combination with other methods for a very pleasant result.

The heat source in these small vessels

In your own home you can continue to enjoy the benefits of this wonderful therapy through its various applications..

causes the scented oils to evaporate and perfume the whole room in which they are located. It is a very pleasant and practical method that enables you to benefit from aromatherapy, because virtually all essential oils have perfumed aromas reminiscent of their origin, whether herbal, balsamic, floral or wood.

Although each session can be aimed at a specific purpose, there is no problem with repeating it as often as you like. Choose the one you like the best, or one that makes you feel the most relaxed, and enjoy it.

There are several types of vessel that can be used to vaporize essential oils. A diffusor is the most common. It can be ceramic, glass or metal. There are many types, and all work according to the same principle. There is a base where a small candle is placed, and a receptacle on top that resembles a plate into which is put a little bit of water and a few drops of essential oils. A metal candleholder is the safest and cleanest because the wax does not spill and the candle goes out once it is consumed. The heat generated by the candle warms the base of the upper receptacle, and the water and essential oil slowly begin to evaporate.

It is best to choose a diffusor with a somewhat deep receptacle so that you can add water as needed. In this way the diffusion of essential oils can last up to two hours. The water helps it to evaporate slowly. This prevents the essential oils from becoming adulterated by excessive heat.

Since a good candle can last about eight hours, you should check from time to time to make sure that there is still enough water in the receptacle to prevent it from getting too hot and cracking. You can replenish the water, add more oils, or simply blow out the candle.

There are some diffusors that have an electric component instead of a candle. These have a great advantage in that they can be left on in a room without needing to be watched, and there is no danger from a candle flame.

If you do not have access to a readymade diffusor, you can improvise one at home. Simply take a plate of very hot water and add one or two drops of essential oil. This method does not last as long as the one mentioned above, but it gets you out of a bind if you need a session and do not have a diffusor at your disposal.

If your house has a steam heating system and radiators, you can make the most of them by aromatizing your entire house. Specialty shops sell small receptacles called "radiator diffusors," and these can be placed on top of your heating source. Just add a little bit of water and a few drops of essential oil and, presto!

You can also decide to use an aromatizer. These are small receptacles that operate by electricity. Water is not necessary, so all you need to do is add the essential oil. All that is needed is an electrical outlet.

And finally, there are ring vaporizers. In this case a metal ring is placed on a light bulb. Place the ring on a flat surface and pour a few drops of essential oil over the groove. After the ring has absorbed the oil, it can be placed on the light bulb, which will serve as the heat source that vaporizes the active ingredients in the essential oil.

With a floor lamp, you don't have to un-screw the bulb. Just place it on top. However, if the bulb is hanging from a ceiling lamp, you must remove it, thread the ring around the narrow part of the bulb, and screw it back into the socket.

This method does not have as many ther-apeutic properties as the others because essential oils evaporate quickly, and the heat counteracts some of the active ingre-dients. Even so, it is a wonderful way to perfume your environment and create an ambience of wellbeing and tranquility.

Inhalation

With inhalation, the source that emits the active ingredients of essential oils is much closer to your nose than with vaporization. Its therapeutic capacity is therefore much higher and more effective. This method of application delivers the benefits of aromatherapy directly to the respiratory tract and from there to the bloodstream.

Essential oils can be inhaled for many ailments, not just those affecting the respiratory tract, but also for headaches, nervousness, insomnia, and depression. They can be applied cold or with steam. In the first case it is recommended to just put a few drops of essential oil on your pillow or handkerchief. The end result will be pleasantly inspiring, yet profound. If you use them on your pillow, you will breathe the oils throughout the night. These will help you to have a restorative rest and to heal while you sleep.

If steam inhalation is prescribed to you, the system is the same as a traditional vaporizer. You fill a bowl with very hot water and add the indicated quantities of the recommended essential oils. Wrap a towel around your head and for several minutes deeply inhale the vapors that rise from the water in the bowl.

Rest for a little while and then do another series of inhalations. If you experience dizziness or any other type of discomfort, stop the procedure. Even though these symptoms can disappear after a few

minutes, they can indicate that you are overheated or that some of the oils you used do not agree with you.

Baths

In either a cold or hot bath, essential oils blend with the water and penetrate the pores of your skin. In addition, the steam generated by hot baths facilitates inhalation of the active ingredients, so they can penetrate the respiratory tract and reach the brain through the nose.

Science has proven that the active ingredients of essential oils are absorbed through the pores of the skin, but this just confirms what was already recommended by Hippocrates in the fourth century BCE, namely that taking an aromatic bath every day is good for the body and soul.

You should never exceed the recommended dose; avoid getting water in your eyes, as this can cause irritation. Six drops are enough for a scented bath, but the dose can be higher if prescribed by your aromatherapist to heal your body and mind.

The oil can be placed in a full bath, or a footbath, a bidet, or a simple bucket depending on your needs, or as advised by a specialist (it could be to treat athlete's foot or to alleviate cystitis).

Once your tub is full of either hot or cold water, add the essential oils and briskly stir to mix them thoroughly with the water just as you are about to submerge. This will allow the maximum benefit from the active ingredients, which evaporate quickly on account of the water temperature. Since essential oils only dissolve in a base of fat, you will see tiny drops distributed throughout the water. A good tip is to mix them beforehand in a glass of milk, where they dissolve easily, and then add the milk to the bath. This is just another way to reap the benefits of aromatherapy and, incidentally, to evoke the legendary Cleopatra. In case you do not want to add milk to the bath, you can dissolve them in a tablespoon of vegetable oil, such as grape seed, and add this to the bath afterwards. Even if your pores don't absorb the essential oils in equal measure, your skin will be grateful.

If you take a bath to relax, you can also add a generous amount of bath salts, such as those from the Dead Sea. But if your objective is to soothe arthritis, or to treat depression, it would be best to take a good shower beforehand and afterward fill the bath with only hot water and essential oils since soap, a vegetable oil, and bath salts might inhibit your pores from adequately absorbing the active ingredients.

It is important to remember that after a relaxing bath, it is best not to engage right away in any activity that requires you to be alert, such as driving or working with machines.

Ideally you should to take it just before going to bed as a health benefit and to wind down after an exhausting and stressful day. Below we

the dual benefit and take a shower in the morning and a bath before going to bed, or combine it on alternate days.

The shower is an excellent mode of application for treatments that tone and stimulate. You can apply essential oils to a wet washcloth or a sponge soaked in hot water and rub vigorously, while avoiding sensitive areas. You can also add a few drops of essential oils to the washcloth, and place it at the base of the shower, in the stream of running water. When you open the tap, deeply inhale the vapors that arise from the hot washcloth. In this type of application you should use up to eight drops, while in the first, two or three will suffice.

provide an approximation of the rest periods recommended after bathing. These will vary in accordance with the desired result of the bath you prepare.

If you do not have a bathtub at your disposal, you can opt to take an aromatherapy shower. Although the results are not as effective, it's always a helpful follow up to a session with a beautician or aromatherapist. If you have both a shower and a bath, you can take advantage of

Periods of repose

Stimulation	20 minutes (cold bath)
General	30 minutes
Depression	45 minutes
Arthritis, muscle pain	1 hour
Relaxation	1 to 2 hours
Mental or physical fatigue	1 to 2 hours
Aphrodisiac	As much time as you like.

Massage

Next to the bath, massage is one of the most common and useful applications for aromatherapy. Not only is it a way to get the essential oils to penetrate the skin, because they are always dissolved in a base oil, but the repetitive motion of the massage enhances the therapeutic effect, which helps to relax the muscles, and stimulate the circulatory and lymphatic systems. And, in addition, massage has the power to calm the mind. Indeed, whether partial or total, it is usually associated with the pleasure of relaxation and physical and emo-

tional wellbeing. A bad day that ends with a good massage is not a bad day because tensions are alleviated, positive emotions are generated, and one can set aside those bad moments caused by stress or problems.

On the other hand, by using a mixture of vegetable oil and essential oils, you can get the active ingredients of both to enter your body by two different routes: the bloodstream and brain. In the same way that they penetrate the skin, the capillaries conduct them to the major veins and distribute them throughout the body. In addition, when the person who receives the massage smells them, they reach the lymphatic system, which in turn conducts them to the part of the body that needs them most. If a massage is for a specific physical problem in a particular area the benefits of essential oils are almost immediate in the affected area as they begin to "work" to alleviate the condition. If the purpose of the massage is to ease a negative emotion, such as depression, sadness or anger, the effects are also very positive. This results not only from aromatherapy itself, but also by the way it is applied. You feel valued by the person who is giving the massage, and totally relaxed by the comforting dynamic of the session.

This last point is important. To give a full body massage that is truly effective, the place where the session will be held should be prepared beforehand. There is a difference between massaging an arm or a foot and a total massage. The former is appropriate if there is a very localized pain or injury. But the latter aims at improvements on a much deeper internal level, a cure from the inside out. In these cases, massage is the vehicle through which essential

A bad day that ends with a good massage is not such a bad day because it releases tensions, generates positive emotions, and makes you forget the bad moments.

How to prepare your own dilutions

Throughout the chapters in which we describe physical illness and negative emotions we propose some aromatherapy remedies that you can apply at home in the form of massage. You should adhere to the amounts indicated. If you want to change the essential oil or doseage, you should consult an aromatherapist. In preparing home remedies, cooking utensils may work better than test tubes and scales. To facilitate this, we provide the approximate equivalent measurements:

- 60 ml = 4 tablespoons
- 30 ml = 2 tablespoons
- 15 ml = 1 tablespoon
- 10 ml = 1 dessert spoon
- 5 ml = 1 teaspoon
- small dropper: 24 drops = 1 ml
- large dropper: 12 drops = 1 ml

In stores you can find droppers corresponding to some of the measurements that we propose, including 125 ml. However, we recommend that you do not prepare large quantities of the solutions, since natural products can easily become rancid. Remember that when you prepare or buy solutions for aromatherapy they should be packaged in dark bottles. The best ones are brown with a dropper to facilitate dosage. It is important that they be hermetically sealed containers with screw caps to prevent evaporation of the essential oils. In addition, they should be stored away from light and heat, in order to prolong their shelf life at optimal potency. A carrier oil should last for six months, but this period can be considerably prolonged if you add a few drops of wheat germ oil. It contains vitamin E, which acts as a natural preservative for the solution. Essential oils, on the other hand, can last for up to six years although in general, they should not be kept for longer than two, and citrus oils have an even shorter shelf life.

Warnings about massage

Although it can seem easy and harmless, massage is a powerful therapeutic tool that should be skillfully applied, and is not beneficial for everyone. There are some conditions for which it is not recommended.:

● **In cases of thrombosis,** hematoma, or an inflammatory condition, the area should not be massaged.

● **A massage should not be given** to someone with epilepsy, high stress, diabetes, fever, heart problems, or a contagious disease.

● **If after a few minutes after beginning a back-massage** a pain starts that extends to the arms or legs, you should stop immediately and consult a physician. If the pain is already present prior to the massage, it should not be performed, because this might aggravate the condition.

● **If the skin over the area that you want to massage** is bruised, swollen, or infected, it is better to apply compresses.

● **It is not advisable to massage varicose veins** because they are very delicate. If you are massaging the whole leg, it is better to use the palms of your hands and not press hard with your fingertips.

● **You should not use essential oils when massaging a pregnant woman** until after the fourth month of her term. But after that, it can be very beneficial. If it is uncomfortable for her to lie face down, she can sit backwards on a chair, supporting her belly on a cushion, resting her arms. This will be comfortable, and you can massage her back without difficulty.

● **You should not give or receive a massage after eating.** Please wait for a couple of hours, because all of the energy in your body is concentrated on the digestive process, and you might hinder it. It is also not advisable if your energy is low, or if you feel ill.

oils locate the problem in your body and mind, and begin to act.

In order to make it "magical," the room where the massage takes place should be just right. It must be a quiet, either silent or with soft music, and a comfortable temperature so that cold does not contract the muscles or hinder the wellbeing produced by the massage. In addition, it should not be merely a comfortable

propriate height and can work on both sides. Once the room is prepared, you should take some breaths to relax and, above all, be ready to give or receive a massage. The good disposition of both people is critical because it is not only a massage, it is an exchange of energies between the giver and the recipient, and it should be as positive as possible.

If your partner asks you for a massage, and you are not in the mood either due to fatigue or because would you rather receive it than give it, you should decline to give it, because it will not be as effective.

Massage is a therapeutic act, but it is also one of pleasure and of surrender that should be equally enjoyable for both the recipient and the giver. Once the conditions are favorable, pour some of the oil mixture into your hands and rub the oil to heat it and so that it can be distributed evenly. It goes without saying that every skin is different and needs a different amount of oil according to its level of hydration. This should therefore be adapted to the person, more oil added or the session prolonged until the oil has been well absorbed. Also, you should use your whole palm and maintain short fingernails so as not to cause any scratches. Finally, you can cover the area that is not being massaged with towels so that the recipient is not cold and is completely relaxed.

room, but a place that is as relaxing as possible for the subject.

If you do it at home and do not have a table, you can put some blankets on the floor and do it on your knees, although you might find this position is uncomfortable after a while. A simple and practical solution is to put blankets on a table, for example the dining room table, so that the person giving the massage is at an ap-

Massage techniques

Massage is a linked sequence of movements administered to different parts of the body. Although it might seem complicated at first, the truth is that you should do it gently and make it almost like a playful act, without fear. The touch of your hands massaging with aromatic oil is a therapeutic gesture, so do not make it over complicated. Improvise if the situation requires it. There are three basic massage movements: effleurage, kneading, and thumb friction.

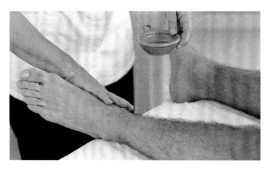

EFFLEURAGE

The technique of effleurage is characteristic of aromatherapy, which advocates gentle and relaxing massages. It is used in the initial and final stages of all massages and consists of a slow, soft, and rhythmic movement applied by the entire palm in an upward motion, either in a straight trajectory or from side to side, and down. In the first case you can apply more pressure for the greatest impact on the circulatory and lymphatic systems and muscles. Less pressure applied during the downward motion is very relaxing and pleasant. This applies equally to the back, legs, arms and torso. First keep your fingers together and vertical. Then open your fingers and slide your hands in an upward trajectory.

KNEADING

The kneading motion is a technique that is reserved especially for the top of the shoulders, the lower back, legs, and arms. You "knead" the muscles with your fingers or with your whole palm, as though they were dough. It basically consists of a twisting and pinching motion. This relaxes the area and helps to increase blood circulation and eliminate toxins. It can be complemented with a squeezing motion, in which you should grasp the calf or arm with both hands and simulate the movement of wringing a cloth. Do this softly and with the whole hand. In areas where there is less muscle mass you should only use your fingertips.

These techniques are used more often in other types of massages. In aromatherapy, they supplement the session, the main purpose of which is to massage and relax the area while ensuring that the carrier of the essential oil penetrates well.

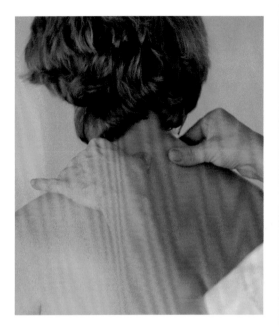

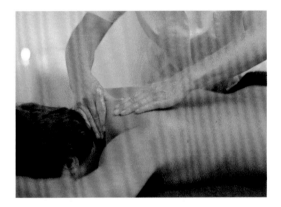

THUMB FRICTION

Finally, the third technique is not so much a movement as pressure applied by the thumbs in a downward motion. It helps to use your body weight when applying it, but always gently so as not to cause any discomfort in the person receiving the massage. You can target a specific location, or apply it in a circular motion. It is usually applied along both sides of the spine (not on top of the spine) in the shoulder region and the back of the thighs. A good session should begin and end exclusively with effleurage, with the other two techniques applied at your discretion. Although we will give you some guidance on the order that applies to a massage sequence, it is important that you follow your intuition to achieve the best results for the person receiving the massage. If in the course of practice you find an area under the skin where tension has accumulated in the form of a "knot" or stiffness, you should not press hard, as this can cause pain. It is best to massage the surrounding area and apply pressure repeatedly, but gently, to the contacted area to try to relax it.

Holistic massage sequence

As we have seen, holistic massage requires a suitable environment. The room should be kept at a comfortable temperature. You should cover the areas that are not being worked on to make the recipient feel better.

For example, when you are massaging the legs, cover the torso with a towel. Remember that it is very important that you apply the massage gently, especially if you are not already an expert in the techniques that you practice.

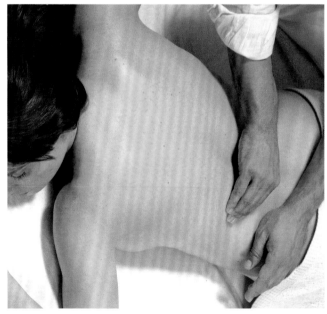

1 **Begin by massaging the back using the three techniques discussed above.** The back is an ideal place to start because it is a large area and conducive to relaxation. In addition, it is a great way to connect with the person you are massaging.

2 **Continuing, cover the back and uncover one leg.** Massage it, cover it, and continue on to the
other. Kneading is a good technique for this area. After having worked the back of the legs, continue
on to the front.

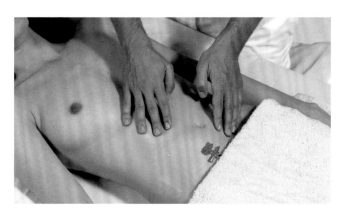
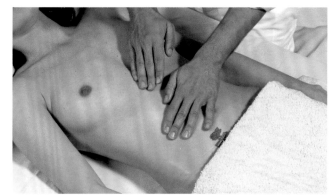

3 **Next, cover the lower body and massage the stomach using the thumb friction technique.** This
area should be massaged in a circular motion in a clockwise direction in order to aid digestion.

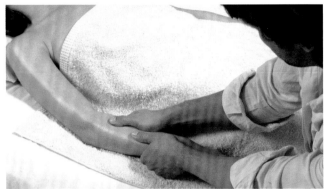

4 **The arms can be massaged a bit more firmly. Always work from the shoulder to the hands.** This area is suited to the kneading technique with a twisting and pinching motion. When working the shoulders, remember that it is better to apply the thumb friction technique.

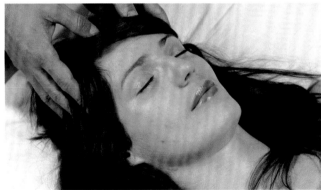

5 **Massaging the face and scalp should be done with fingertips only. It is necessary that the massage here be very delicate.** You can perform all of the techniques that we explained in the previous section, including thumb friction in a circular motion, but avoid the eye area, because the oils are irritating.

Cosmetic applications

Along with baths and facials, massage is the main technique used for cosmetic aromatherapy. However, when you apply a remedy to a cosmetic purpose such as improving the appearance of your skin or combating cellulite, you will also be helping your body and mind on a very deep level. Massage increase blood circulation, relaxes the muscles, and dissipates negative emotions such as sadness or anxiety. Thus in addition to beauty as an end result, you will also enhance your wellbeing. Although the cosmetic benefits of aromatherapy are not the aim of this book, we will take the opportunity to mention some effective remedies that will help you become more beautiful or handsome both inside and out.

Tips

● **Put a diffusor with some relaxing essential oils** in your room to help create a comfortable atmosphere.

● **Maintain the same rhythm** throughout a massage so as not to break the recipient's state of relaxation.

● **Massage is, above all, a time of relaxation** and communion between two people. Soft music can contribute to the experience, but avoid speaking so as not to distract one another. It is better to concentrate the mind on the movements being given and received.

● **Throughout the massage,** it is good to maintain one hand in contact with the person who is receiving it so as not to interrupt the exchange of energies. A good

massage should have a relaxed, but steady, rhythm.

● **A holistic massage** usually takes an hour and a half, but if you do not have much time, you can concentrate on the areas that recipient needs most, like the back, for example.

● **Start with gentle movements,** then increase the pressure of your hands, and, finally, return to a gentle motion.

● **Use the weight of your own body** to help with the motions that require more pressure.

Cellulite and water retention

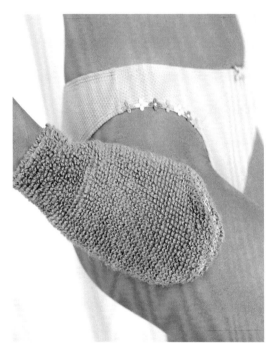

ering, every day for one month. Take a break for four days and the continue the next month using the following mixture: 50 ml. of grape seed oil, 6 drops of lavender, 6 of patchouli, 6 of rosemary, and 6 of cypress. For the duration of this treatment, take a bath twice a week in water that is not too hot with 6 drops of juniper. Thoroughly coat a rough bath mitt with orange peel before applying the massage oil. This stimulates circulation, helps to eliminate water retention, and opens your pores to optimally absorb the essential oils.

Aromatherapy remedies

Any of the recommended oils are ideal when 8 to 10 drops are added to bath water and have a beneficial effect on cellulite and water retention.

Kneading is the best massage technique for cellulite. Mix 50 ml. of grape seed oil and add 6 drops of geranium, 6 of juniper, 6 of lemon, and 4 of fennel. Massage the areas after show-

Recommended essential oils

- Angelica
- Cedar
- Cypress
- Fennel
- Geranium
- Grapefruit
- Juniper
- Lavender
- Lemon
- Lime
- Mandarin
- Patchouli
- Pine
- Rosemary
- Sandalwood

Hair

Dry hair
Aromatherapy remedies

● To make a good solution mix 50 ml. of sweet almond oil with 5 drops of mild shampoo.

Recommended essential oils

● Chamomile (blonde hair)
● Lavender
● Rosemary (brown hair)

Oily hair
Aromatherapy remedies

● Add up to 6 drops of any of the oils that we recommend, or a mixture of not more than three, in 125 ml. of mild shampoo.

Recommended essential oils

● Clary Sage
● Cypress
● Geranium
● Lavender
● Lemon
● Rosemary
● Tea Tree

Dandruff
Aromatherapy remedies

● **For dry hair,** mix 30 ml. of sweet almond oil with 5 drops of geranium, 5 of lavender, and 5 of sandalwood. Apply it to the scalp with a gentle massage and leave it in for two hours or, better yet, overnight. Then lather it well and rinse with water to which you've added the same quantities of essential oils. Repeat the treatment every two days until your scalp improves. Then you need apply it only twice a week until the problem disappears.

● **For oily hair,** mix 30 ml. of grape seed oil with 6 drops of cedar, 4 of rosemary, and 4 of lemon. Apply the treatment exactly as described above for dry hair.

Recommended essential oils

● Cedar
● Geranium
● Juniper
● Lavender
● Lemon
● Patchouli
● Rosemary
● Sandalwood
● Tea tree

Different types of skin

Oily skin
Aromatherapy remedies

You can make a cleansing lotion with 100 ml. of lavender water, 15 ml. of glycerin, 7 drops of lavender essential oil, 7 of geranium, 3 of bergamot, and 3 of sandalwood.

- You can mix 20 ml. of cider vinegar with 80 ml. of rose water and add 5 drops of lavender. This tonic cleans and revitalizes the skin.
- To hydrate the skin, mix 25 ml. of apricot kernel oil or a neutral cream with 15 ml. of wheat germ oil, 3 drops of lavender essential oil, 3 of geranium, and 3 of patchouli or palmarosa.
- Finally you can make a mask with 25 ml. clay paste to which you've added 2 drops of tea tree essential oil, 2 of lavender and 2 of bergamot,

and apply it a couple of times a week.

Dry or mixed skin
Aromatherapy remedies

You can make a restorative tonic with the following mixture: in a dark bottle put 75 ml. of rose water, 7 drops of chamomile essential oil, 7 of lavender, and 7 of sandalwood. Let it sit for a

Recommended essential oils

Basil	Grapefruit	Patchouli
Bergamot	Juniper	Petitgrain
Cedar	Lavender	Rosemary
Chamomile	Lemongrass	Rosewood
Clary sage	Lime	Sandalwood
Cypress	Mandarin	Tea Tree
Eucalyptus	Neroli	Vetiver
Geranium	Palmarosa	

month. Then filter it with a coffee filter, add 25 ml. of glycerin and stir it well. Apply it twice a day.

● To hydrate and nourish the skin you can mix 25 ml. of apricot kernel oil, 15 ml. of avocado, evening primrose oil, or wheat germ oil, and 3 drops of rose essential oil, 3 of lavender, and 3 more of geranium or palmarosa.

● You can make a natural restorative mask to be applied two or three times a week. The mixture consists of 35 ml. of clay, 10 ml. of honey, 10 ml. of cornstarch, 1 egg yolk, 5 ml. of evening primrose oil, and two drops of rose essential oil, 2 of lavender, and 2 of sandalwood. After leaving it on for fifteen minutes, rinse your skin with cold water.

Recommended essential oils

- Cedar
- Chamomile
- Geranium
- Jasmine
- Lavender
- Myrrh
- Neroli
- Patchouli
- Rose
- Rosewood
- Sandalwood
- Tea Tree
- Yarrow
- Ylang Ylang

Sensitive or couperose skin
Aromatherapy remedies

To clean the skin, you should avoid using strong soaps. It is better to make a preparation of 75 ml. of rose water, 5 drops of chamomile essential oil, 5 of lavender, and 3 of rose. Let it sit for a month in a dark, hermetically sealed container. Then, filter it through a coffee filter, and add 25 ml. of glycerin. Stir the mixture well, and apply it with cotton, morning and night, after having moisturized the skin.

● To hydrate the skin well, make a preparation of 25 ml. of jojoba or apricot kernel oil with 3 drops of rose essential oil and 3 of chamomile or lavender. If you have couperose skin, mix 15 ml. of hypoallergenic cream with 3 drops of rose essential oil and liberally massage the affected area twice a day.

● Another mixture that helps rejuvenate sensitive or blotchy skin consists of 100 ml. of neroli oil to which have been added 2 drops of rose essential oil, 2 of neroli or petitgrain, and 2 of lavender.

● We do not recommend clay masks. Honey is better, being gentler and more moisturizing.

Couperosis (or "red veins") is caused by poor irrigation in the capillaries of the facial skin and is particularly noticeable on the nose, cheeks and forehead.

Recommended essential oils

- Carrot
- Chamomile
- Jasmine
- Lavender
- Neroli
- Petitgrain
- Rose
- Yarrow

massage it into your skin, avoiding the eyelids so as not to irritate the eyes. After five minutes, re-move the excess with a paper towel.

● Wheat germ oil is excellent for the contours of the eyes, but to prevent it from getting into eyes themselves, it should be massaged in circles around the cheekbone without touching the cor-ners of the eyes or eyelids.

● A very suitable tonic for this type of skin is rose water enriched with essential oils. Add 75 ml. of hydrolate, 7 drops of geranium, 7 of lavender, 3 of neroli, and 3 of frankincense.

Dull or aging skin
Aromatherapy remedies

An ideal mixture for nourishing the skin is: 25 ml. of jojoba, sweet almond or grape seed oil, or a cream with a neutral base, and 15 ml. of wheat germ oil, plus 15 ml. of evening primrose oil. Then add 10 to 15 drops in total of lavender, rose in-cense, and neroli. Shake the container, and mix five drops of the solution with a little bit of warm water in the palm of your hand. Rub your hands together to emulsify the mixture and gently

Recommended essential oils

- Carrot
- Clary sage
- Chamomile
- Cypress
- Geranium
- Incense
- Juniper
- Jasmine
- Lavender
- Myrrh
- Neroli
- Palmarosa
- Patchouli
- Rosewood
- Rose
- Rosemary
- Sandalwood
- Ylang Ylang

Other applications

Compresses

This form of applying aromatherapy remedies is very useful for treating small areas, inflammation, and headaches or fever. For each case we will be explaining how you should prepare the compress, either hot or cold, and listing the right mix of essential oils for each illness or negative emotion. In preparation, you should choose a pure cotton towel or cloth, and if possible, free of dyes in order to avoid irritating very sensitive skins. Having chosen the material, soak it in the water to which you have added the recommended essential oils, and place it over the affected area.

To enhance the effect of a hot compress put a hot water bottle or a blanket over it. This prolongs the benefit of the heat and active ingredients of the essential oils in the area you are treating.

Gargles

You should only gargle in those cases recommended by an aromatherapist. These can be very effective in treating sore throats and gums, but it is very important that you do not swallow the liquid since some essential oils are irritants and can produce internal lesions.

For different conditions where it may be useful to gargle we have provided the remedy and the corresponding method, so you can also benefit from this aromatherapeutic application.

The main essential oils

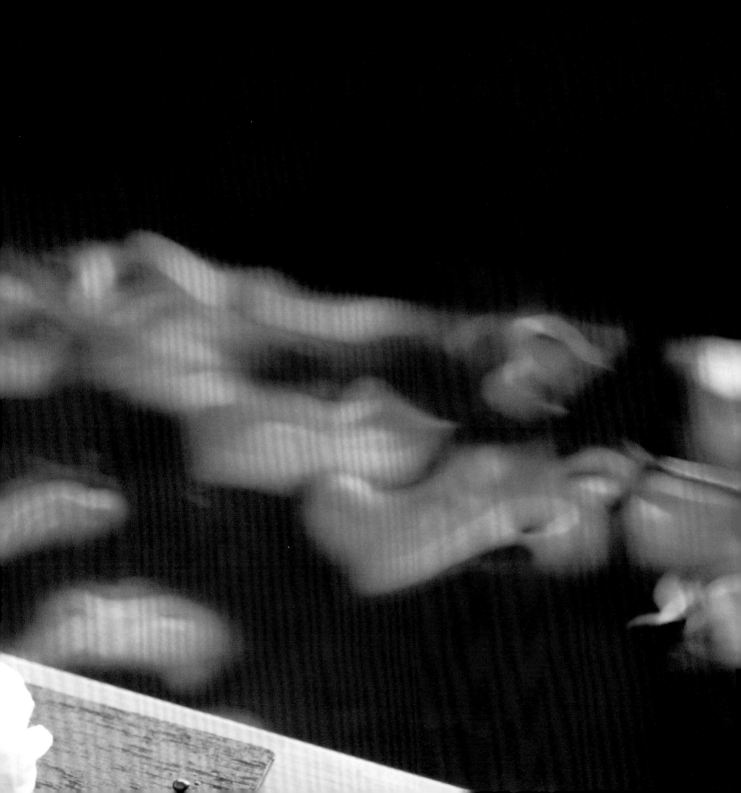

Essential oils: a safe therapy

Essential oils are an extraordinary source of therapeutic and cosmetic benefits of natural origin. They are treasures that nature puts at our disposal through different processes and that can be applied in different ways.

The word "natural," however, is not always synonymous with harml.ess and beneficial. Plant products can be very powerful and should always be recommended or applied by a therapist whom you trust. And this recommendation is not limited to essential oils, but also refers to herbal medicine, Bach flowers or any other natural therapeutic product.

If you follow the advice of the specialist and use moderation and common sense, aromatherapy can only bring benefits, great benefits, to your body and mind. Used well, it could be your companion to overcome problematic physical and emotional states, as we will describe to you in the final chapters of this book. However, we want to emphasize the series of steps and advice that we gave you in the previous chapter, so that you can avoid abuse or misuse of essential oils, and the negative consequences this could have on your health and emotions.

In addition, we provide a list of essential oils

that can be toxic. There are manufacturers who market them for use in cosmetics, perfumes, and the home, but not for therapy or emotional wellbeing. We absolutely discourage their use so as to avoid any type of risk. This toxicity is in many cases determined by the active ingredients that are generated in the extraction process, and are, sometimes, not in the plant from which they are extracted.

In other cases, the process of extraction by

volatile solvents renders them unusable for use in therapy because there are small traces of these chemicals, although they are completely normal in perfumery.

The list of "safe" essential oils that we provide at the end of this chapter is extensive, and we are convinced that it includes all your physical and emotional needs for when you require treatment with aromatherapy. So avoid the oils discussed below, and enjoy those described later.

Oils to Avoid

We should say that the International Association of Aromatherapists endorses the essential oils discussed here, although they represent a risk if used incorrectly. On the other hand, their derivative plants can be safely used both in herbal medicine and homeopathy as well as in your kitchen. We emphasize that the list below only refers specifically to essential oils, and these plants can otherwise still be used with peace of mind in infusions or in recipes, and some of them can be taken with confidence in remedies prescribed by your homeopath.

List of oils to avoid

Arnica
Arnica montana
Bitter Almond
prunus dulcis var. amara
Boldo Leaf
Peumus boldus
Buchu
Barosma betulina
Calamus
Acorus calamus
Camphor, brown and yellow
Cinnamomum camphora
Chervil
Anthriscus cerefolium
Cinnamon Bark
Cinnamomum cassia
Common Broom
Cytisus scoparius
Croton
Croton tiglium, C.

oblongifolius
Daffodil
Narcissus poeticus
Dwarf Mugo Pine
Pinus pumilio, P. mugo
Gaultheria
Gaultheria procumbens
Goosefoot
Chenopodium ambrosioides
Horseradish
Cochlearia armoracia
Jaborandi
Pilocarpus microphyllus
Melilot
Melilotus officinalis
Mugwort
Artemisia vulgaris
Mustard
Brassica spp. esp. B. Nigra y B. juncea
Parsley
Petroselenium crispum

Pennyroyal
Menta pulegium
Perilla
Perilla frutescens
Rue
Ruta graveolens
Sassafras
Sassafras albidum
Savin Juniper
Juniperus sabina
Summer Savory
Satureja hortensis
Tansy
Tanacetum vulgare
Thuja
Thuja occidentalis
Tonka Bean
Dipteryx odorata oppositifolia
White Wormwood
Artemisia herba-alba
Wormwood
Artemisia absinthium

Glossary of therapeutic properties

In this glossary we list very briefly the main therapeutic characteristics that essential oils may have so as to make it easier for you to consult than the wide range of sixty oils we provide subsequently.

These are technical terms used in medicine, pharmaceuticals and natural therapies, found throughout this book.

- **Abortifacient**
May be used to induce a miscarriage
- **Analgesic**
Soothes pain
- **Analgesic (dental)**
Alleviates toothaches
- **Anaphrodisiac**
Decreases sexual desire
- **Anesthetic**
Contributes to the loss of sensation and relieves pain
- **Anodyne**
Reduces or relieves pain
- **Antacid**
Reduces the production of acid
- **Anthelmintic**
Kills and expels intestinal worms
- **Anti-allergenic**
Helps calm the symptoms of allergies
- **Anti-anemic**
Helps counteract anemia
- **Anti-arthritic**
Alleviates arthritis
- **Anti-bilious**
Helps eliminate excess bile
- **Antibiotic**
Combats bacteria
- **Anti-catarrhal**
Relieves cold symptoms
- **Anticoagulant**
Thins the blood to prevent the formation of clots
- **Anticonvulsant**
Helps to control seizures
- **Antidepressant**
Neutralizes melancholy and promotes euphoria
- **Anti-diarrheal**
Stops diarrhea
- **Antiemetic**
Helps control nausea and vomiting
- **Antigalactagogue**
Reduces the flow of breast milk
- **Antihemorrhagic**
Helps stop bleeding
- **Antihistamine**
Relieves symptoms produced by the release of histamine in allergies
- **Anti-infective**
Combats infection
- **Anti-inflammatory**
Relieves inflammation
- **Antilitico**
Reduces the risk of forming kidney stones
- **Antimicrobial**
Eliminates microbes
- **Antineuralgic**
Relieves pain caused by nerve inflammation
- **Antioxidant**

Reduces and prevents the aging of tissues

- **Antiparasitic**
Combats parasites

- **Antiphlogistic**
Reduces inflammation

- **Antipruritic**
Relieves itching and burning

- **Antiputrefactive**
Delays putrefaction in plant and animal matter

- **Antirheumatic**
Fights the pain and inflammation caused by rheumatism

- **Antiperspirant**
Prevents sweating

- **Antipyretic**
Reduces fever

- **Anti-sclerotic**
Helps lowers the risk of the hardening of the inflamed tissues

- **Anti-scorbutic**
Prevents scurvy

- **Antiseptic**
Prevents the proliferation

of bacteria

- **Antispasmodic**
Reduces spasms and muscle cramps

- **Antitoxic**
Neutralizes the effects of ingesting or inhaling a toxin

- **Antitussive**
Suppresses coughs

- **Anti-venom**
Neutralizes the effects of the venom of snakes, scorpions, and some insects

- **Antiviral**
Inhibits the development of viruses

- **Anti-warts**
Helps reduce and remove warts

- **Aphrodisiac**
Stimulates sexual desire

- **Astringent**
Shrinks or constricts various body tissues

- **Bactericide**
Stops the development and action of bacteria

- **Balsamic**
Alleviates and softens mucus in the lungs

- **Cardiac**
Stimulates the heart

- **Cardiotonic**
Stimulates the heart and increases the tonus of the vascular muscle

- **Carminative**
Calms flatulence and aids the gastrointestinal tract

- **Cephalic**
Soothes and mitigates headaches

- **Cholagogue**
Promotes the flow of bile into the duodenum

- **Choleretic**
Helps increase the secretion of bile

- **Cautery**
Aids healing

- **Comedogenic**
Helps reduce pimples and blisters

- **Cordial**
Simulates the heart

- **Cytophylactic**
Promotes the regeneration of cells
- **Cytotoxic**
Poisons cells
- **Decongestive**
Reduces nasal secretion
- **Deodorant**
Neutralizes body odor
- **Depurant**
Cleanses the blood of toxins
- **Detoxicant**
Eliminates toxic substances
- **Diaphoretic**
Promotes perspiration
- **Digestive**
Aids digestion
- **Disinfectant**
Eliminates germs
- **Diuretic**
Stimulates the elimination of liquids through urination
- **Emmenagogue**
Helps regulate menstruation

- **Emollient**
Softens and hydrates the skin
- **Euphoric**
Produces euphoria and general wellbeing
- **Expectorant**
Promotes the elimination of phlegm and relieves colds
- **Febrifuge**
Calms fever
- **Fungicide**
Combats infections caused by fungus
- **Galactagogue**
Stimulates the flow of breast milk
- **Germicide**
Fights germs and bacteria
- **Hallucinogenic**
Provokes visions and hallucinations
- **Hemostatic**
Stops bleeding and thickens the blood
- **Hepatic**
Stimulates the liver and has an affinity for this organ
- **Hepatotoxic**
Has a toxic effect on the liver
- **Hypertensive**
Increases blood pressure and circulation
- **Hypnotic**
Aids sleep and facilitates trances
- **Hypoglycemic**
Treats diabetes
- **Hypoglycemic**
Lowers blood sugar level
- **Hypotensive**
Reduces blood pressure
- **Immunostimulant**
Boosts the immune system
- **Insecticide**
Kills insects
- **Larvicide**
Kills larvae and prevents their emergence
- **Laxative**
Facilitates intestinal transit

● **Lipolytic**
Reduces body fat

● **Mucolytic**
Liquefies mucus and facilitates its removal

● **Narcotic**
Induces sleep but should not be taken in large doses

● **Nervine**
Has a balancing effect on the nervous system

● **Neurotoxin**
Harms the nervous system

● **Orexigenic**
Simulates appetite

● **Pediculicide**
Helps kill lice and nits

● **Prophylactic**
Helps prevent disease

● **Purgative**
Produces a quick evacuation of the bowel

● **Regulator**
Balances bodily functions

● **Relaxant**
Relieves nervousness

● **Restorative**
Revitalizes and restores

health

● **Rubefacient**
Reddens the skin by activating local blood circulation

● **Sedative**
Relieves nervousness

● **Sialogogue**
Increases the secretion of saliva

● **Soporific**
Induces dreams

● **Spasmolytic**
Relieves muscle spasms and cramps

● **Splenic**
Invigorates the spleen and has affinity with this organ«

● **Stimulant**
Invigorates the body and mind

● **Stomachic**
Relieves stomach disorders and has an affinity with this organ

● **Sudorific**
Stimulates perspiration

● **Tonic**
Tones and revitalizes the body

● **Uterine**
Revitalizes the uterus and has an affinity for this organ

● **Vasoconstrictor**
Constricts blood vessels through local application

● **Vasodilator**
Dilates blood vessels through local application

● **Vulnerary**
Helps heal

The most common essential oils

The essential oils that we describe here may be, in some cases, phototoxic. You should not apply them before sunbathing because they might cause skin blotches.

Others can also cause some irritation or sensitivity in very delicate skin.

All of the previously mentioned cases are noted in the "Advisory" section in the forthcoming pages so that you can make the decision whether to use them or not.

Reactions usually do not occur if the essential oil is diluted in a good carrier oil and in the amounts indicated by the aromatherapist, but it is always better to have all of the information so that you can choose freely.

Advisory
- The essential oil of angelica root can be phototoxic, which means that it can cause skin irritation if exposed to sun. Therefore, do not sunbathe after applying it.
- Do not use if you are pregnant.
- Exceeding the dosage can cause drowsiness and slow your blood circulation.

Angelica

General description

Also known as "Holy Ghost," this is a large plant that can exceed 2 m. in height. Its leaves are bright green, reminiscent of fern, and its flowers, which contain the seeds from which one of its essential oils is extracted, are very aromatic. The fragrance is sweet and tangy with earthy notes.

Its essential oil can be extracted from its root or its seeds. Both are similar, but that from the root is stronger and more concentrated, whereas the seeds contain a higher amount of essential oil. On some occasions they are used separately and sometimes they are combined. The color is transparent at first and turns yellow over time. If it turns brown, it should be discarded.

Latin name:

Angelica archangelica

Family:

Apiaceae

Therapeutic properties of the essential oil

- Antispasmodic
- Aphrodisiac
- Bactericide
- Carminative
- Depurant
- Diuretic
- Emenagogue
- Expectorant
- Fungicide
- Hepatic
- Nervine
- Stimulant
- Stomachic
- Sudorífic
- Tonic

Main chemical components

- Angelic acid, Angelicin, Terebangelene, Borneol, Linalool, Bergapten, Limonene, Phellandrene, Pinene

Therapeutic applications

- Anemia, Anorexia, Arthritis, Chronic Bronchitis, Headache, Sciatica, Scars, Cystitis, Colic, Joint Pain, Toothache, Muscle Pain, Stimulation of the Immune System, Stress, Nervous Fatigue, Flatulence, Gout, Bruises, Wounds, Indigestion, Skin Irritation, Dizziness, Migraine, Runny Nose, Nausea, Pleurisy, Psoriasis, Fluid Retention, Rheumatism.

Cosmetic applications

- Clears blocked pores.

Did you know...?

- *According to an ancient legend, the Archangel Raphael made the benefits of angelica known to a monk, having entrusted him with the knowledge for his honesty and kindness during a serious epidemic.*

Basil

Latin name:
Ocimum basilicum
Family:
Lamiaceae

General description

Although there are many varieties of basil, all have an intense aroma when the leaves are crushed. The plant has dark, hairy green leaves of an oval shape, white flowers, and reaches a height of about 25 cm. Its essential oil, which is extracted from the whole plant by steam distillation, is light greenish yellow, and the scent is of a high note, re-freshing and pleasant. It starts out green and fresh, and then gives way to a warm and spicy aroma with notes of aniseed, reminiscent of a mixture of thyme, licorice, and mint. It acts more on the mind and emotions than on physical as-pects.

Did you know...?

● *In Hindu culture basil is called "tulsi." It is considered a sacred herb, and is therefore used when one is sworn in before a judge. In Greek it is called "okimon" meaning "fast," in reference to the rapidity with which the plant grows. Sometimes it is also called "basilicum," its Latin name. This term comes from "basilicon ," which means "ointment of kings." Aphrodisiac properties are also attributed to it.*

Therapeutic properties of the essential oil

- Antidepressant
- Antiseptic
- Antispasmodic
- Carminative
- Digestive
- Emenagogue
- Expectorant
- Febrífuge
- Nervine
- Stomachic
- Sudorífic
- Tonic

Main chemical components
● Alcohol, Ketones, Phenols and Terpenes: Linalool, Camphor, Borneol, Cineol, Estragole, Eugenol, Pinene, Ocimene, Sabinene, Methyl Chavicol

Therapeutic applications
● Anxiety, Bronchitis, Depression, Fainting, Dys-pepsia, Earaches, Epilepsy, Mental Fatigue, Fever, Hay Fever, Gout, Hiccups, Hysteria, Insomnia, Melancholy, Migraine, Nausea, Paralysis, Nasal Polyps, Regulates Menstrual Cycle, Insect Repel-lent, Cold, Nervous Tension, Whooping Cough, Respiratory Disorders, Vomiting

Cosmetic applications
● Often used in men's cologne and to treat oily skin.

Advisory
- *Do not use if you are pregnant.*
- *Basil should be used only in diluted form.*
- *Only recommended for short-term treatments.*

Benzoin

General description

Benzoin oil is extracted from a tree that is indigenous to South East Asia. Its hairy leaves are oval, and its flowers, fleshy and yellow-green. It grows to a height of 20 m. The essential oil is extracted from the resin, which is very balsamic, through the method of volatile solvents. Of a dull brown color and a viscous consistency, its scent is sweet, intense, and vanilla.

Latin name:

Styrax benzoin

Family:

Styracaceae

Main chemical components

● Cinnamic Acid, Vanillin, Coniferyl Benzoate, Benzoic Acid, Phenyl Propyl Alcohol, and Phenylethylene

Therapeutic applications

● Arthritis, Asthma, Bronchitis, Dermatitis, Stress, Gout, Flu, Wounds, Laryngitis, Skin Lesions, Poor Circulation, Pruritus, Psoriasis, Rheumatism, Nervous Tension, Cough

Did you know...?

● *Benzoin has for centuries also been used as incense in churches and for magical rituals.*

Advisory

● *If you are pregnant, you can use benzoin essential oil starting from the fourth month of gestation. However, it is not recommended for babies.*

● *You should make a preliminary test on the skin to see if you have an allergic reaction, which is not the result of the benzoin itself, but of the solvent used in the extraction.*

Therapeutic properties of the essential oil

● Anti-inflammatory	● Deodorant
● Antioxidant	● Diuretic
● Antiseptic	● Expectorant
● Astringent	● Sedative
● Carminative	● Vulnerary
● Cordial	

Cosmetic applications

● Helps to diminish spots on the face, hands, and chest, especially when combined with lemon essential oil. It is also an excellent tonic for sensitive and irritated skin.

● In addition, in perfumery benzoin is used as a fixative for fragrances.

Cajeput

General description

Also known as "cayeput" or "melaleuca," its essential oil is extracted from a tree that was originally indigenous to India but is now found mainly in tropical regions of Australia and Southeast Asia. It came to the West in the seventeenth century, but it had been used in the East for its medicinal properties long before.

The oil is extracted by distillation of the leaves, buds and sprouts, and is almost transparent, although it has a pungent and spicy aroma, reminiscent of pepper, eucalyptus and camphor.

Latin name:
Melaleuca leucadendron
Family:
Myrtaceae

Main chemical components
● Cineol, Benzoic Aldehyde, Butyric Acid, Valeric Acid, Pinene, and Terpineol

Advisory
● *This essential oil is ideal for treating colds in children, but it should never be ingested. It is for external use only.*
● *If you are pregnant, you can use it starting from the fourth month of gestation.*

Therapeutic properties of the essential oil

● **Analgesic**
● **Anthelmintic**
● **Antimicrobial**
● **Antineuralgic**
● **Antipyretic**
● **Antiseptic**
● **Antispasmodic**
● **Carminative**
● **Depurative**
● **Expectorant**
● **Insecticide**
● **Purifiying**
● **Sudorific**
● **Tonic**
● **Venous decongestant**

Therapeutic applications
● Analgesic, Antispasmodic, Antimicrobial, Antineuralgic, Antipyretic, Antiseptic, Carminative, Expectorant, Venous Decongestant, Insecticide, Depurative, Sudorific, Tonic, Anthelmintic

Cosmetic applications
● This is very useful for preventing skin lesions caused by radiation treatments.
● It is also very useful for alleviating any type of cutaneous eruption, and for treating skin that has acne or impurities.

Bergamot

General description

Bergamot oil is extracted from the rind of a citrus fruit native to southern Italy that is reminiscent of a lime, although it is pear shaped. It is much smaller than other citrus fruits, and its color is a golden yellow. The leaves are long, flat, and oval, and the flowers white. The tree does not exceed 4 m. and is a hybrid created that was created centuries ago, being on record since the Middle Ages. The oil, which is extracted by cold expression, is of an emerald green tone, and the aroma is spicy and fresh at the same time, reminiscent of lavender and lemon.

Latin name:
Citrus bergamia
Family:
Rutaceae

Main chemical components
● Linalyl Acetate, Bergamottin, Bergapten, Limonene, and Linalool

Did you know...?
● *Bergamot is an excellent natural insect repellent.*
● *The name of the tree is "bergamot" because it was in the city of Bergamo (Italy) where its essence was first marketed.*

Therapeutic applications
● Abscesses, Anxiety, Bronchitis, Gallstones, Uterine Cancer, Carbuncles, Cystitis, Colic, Depression, Diphtheria, Dyspepsia, Eczema, Stomatitis, Stress, Mental Fatigue, Fever, Flatulence, Glossitis, Gonorrhea, Flu, Halitosis, Sores, Herpes, Loss of Appetite, Respiratory Infections, Urinary Tract Infections, Leucorrhea, Wounds, Intestinal Parasites, Insect Bites, Vaginal Itching, Psoriasis, Colds, Scabies, Nervous Tension, Tonsillitis, Tuberculosis, Varicose Ulcers

Cosmetic applications

● Its antiseptic and rubefacient properties produce very good results in the treatment of skin suffering from acne. It is also recommended for oily hair and skin.

● Moreover, the essence of bergamot is one of the most widely used in perfumery as a base for eau de cologne on account of its sweet and citrusy aroma, very fresh and reminiscent of lavender.

Therapeutic properties of the essential oil

- Analgesic
- Anthelmintic
- Antidepressant
- Antipyretic
- Antiseptic
- Antispasmodic
- Carminative
- Cautery
- Deodorant
- Digestive
- Diuretic
- Expectorant
- Insecticide
- Rubefacient
- Sedative
- Stimulant
- Tonic
- Vulnerary

Black Pepper

General description

Black pepper is obtained from a vine that was originally cultivated in Southeast Asia. It can be up to 6 m. high; it has heart-shaped, dark green leaves and tiny white flowers. Black peppercorns are the berries, which are still green when collected; then they are dried in the sun.

The essential oil is extracted from crushed pepper berries by distillation. Its color ranges from transparent to yellow-green, and its characteristic aroma is spicy, camphor, masculine, oriental, warm, and sensual.

Latin name:
Piper nigrum
Family:
Piperaceae

Main chemical components
- Phellandrene, Pinene, Limonene, and Piperine.

Therapeutic properties of the essential oil

- **Analgesic**
- **Antispasmodic**
- **Antimicrobial**
- **Antirheumatic**
- **Antiseptic**
- **Antitoxic**
- **Aphrodisiac**
- **Bactericide**
- **Carminative**
- **Digestive**
- **Diuretic**
- **Febrifuge**
- **Laxative**
- **Orexigenic**
- **Rubefacient**
- **Stimulant**
- **Stomachic**
- **Tonic (spleen)**

Advisory
- *Always use this essential oil diluted to at most 1% in a vegetable oil carrier because it can be irritating if applied directly to the skin.*

Therapeutic applications
- Heartburn, Anemia, Angina, Arthritis, Sciatica, Cholera, Colic, Dermatitis, Diarrhea, Dysentery, Dyspepsia, Dysuria (difficulty urinating), Toothache, Muscle Pain, Muscle Spasms, Constipation, Fever, Hay Fever, Flatulence, Flu, Loss of Appetite, Indigestion, Viral Infection, Poor Circulation, Nausea, Neuralgia, Colds, Rheumatism, Chilblains, Cough, Nervous Disorders, Dizziness, Vomiting.

Did you know…?
- *In Roman times pepper came to be more expensive than gold and was highly prized for its culinary and medicinal qualities. This has given rise to popular sayings in many cultures, such as the French phrase, "It is more expensive than pepper."*

Caraway

General description

This plant, related to cumin and coriander, has leaves similar to the carrot plant and grows to a height of around 60 cm. Its white or pink flowers have seeds resembling those of cumin, and it is from these that the essential oil is distilled. This oil, transparent and with some yellow highlights, takes on color over time. Its scent is fruitier and warmer than that of cumin, reminiscent of musk.

Latin name:
Carum carvi
Family:
Umbelliferae

Main chemical components
● Carvone, Arcavol, Carvene, Limonene

Advisory
● *It is completely harmless and can even be used by infants. All you need to do is mix 12 drops of caraway essential oil with 2 drops of wheat germ oil and 50 ml. of sweet almond oil. Then slightly warm up the mixture, and massage the baby's stomach in a circular, clockwise movement.*

Therapeutic applications
● Infant Colic, Colic, Colitis, Dysmenorrhea, Dyspepsia, Abdominal Pain, Flatulence, Loss of Appetite, Indigestion, Bloating, Palpitations, Intestinal Parasites, Vertigo.

Cosmetic applications
● Perfumes, Soaps and Toothpastes

Did you know...?
● *The caraway plant is as old as mankind, and many fossilized seeds have been found at European Neolithic sites. This seed has been used by all cultures for cooking, and its digestive and culinary properties have been widely recognized.*

Therapeutic properties of the essential oil

● Anthelmintic	● Galactogogue
● Antispasmodic	● Orexigenic
● Carminative	● Stimulant
● Diuretic	● Stomachic
● Emenagogue	● Tonic

Cardamom

General description

Cardamom is a large perennial herbaceous plant belonging to the same family as ginger. It is indigenous to southern India and Sri Lanka, but also grows in China and Indochina. Its rhizome is big and fleshy, and its large leaves have a silky texture. However, its flowers are small, like its fruit, and the essential oil is distilled from the seeds. Being pale yellow, it is almost transparent. Its perfume is warm, fragrant, and spicy, reminiscent of balsamic woods.

In addition to culinary uses, it has great therapeutic applications. It helps fight infections and regulate fluid retention, and it serves as a tonic for those affected by emotional problems: all in all, broad spectrum for an ancient essential oil.

Latin name:
*Elettaria
cardamomum*
Family:
Zingiberaceae

Did you know...?
● *In India cardamom has been used as a spice and as a medicine for many centuries; it is one of the main Ayurvedic herbs. Its rich fragrant aroma has earned it a place in the classic odes of poets such as Ovid.*

Therapeutic properties of the essential oil

● **Antiseptic**	● **Cephalic**
● **Antispasmodic**	● **Digestive**
● **Aphrodisíac**	● **Diuretic**
● **Carminative**	● **Stomachic**

Advisory
● *Cardamom oil is non-toxic, non-irritating and non-sensitizing. You can use it throughout pregnancy without any problems.*

Main chemical components
● Cineol, Terpineol, Limonene, Eucalyptol, and Zingiberene.

Therapeutic applications
● Anorexia, Headache, Colic, Weakness, Dyspepsia, Mental Fatigue, Flatulence, Halitosis, Anorexia, Menopause, Menstruation, Nausea, Heartburn, Coughing, Vomiting

Cosmetic applications
● It is widely used in the composition of floral perfumes for its sweet, spicy, and long-lasting aroma. In addition, because of its capacity to freshen breath and prevent halitosis, it is added to toothpastes.

Carrot

General description

Carrots are a treasure trove of vitamins and carotene, which was a precursor to vitamins. Known since ancient times, it is a biennial plant with a hard root and feathery green leaves. It can be orange, white, red, or purple, as there are many varieties grown, hybrid from the original, native to Afghanistan, which was small, whitish, hard, and very long.

   The essential oil is extracted from dried seeds by steam distillation. Amber in color, the texture is very liquid, and the aroma is spicy, dry, and warm, with earthy and herbaceous notes.

Latin name:
Daucus carota
Family:
Umbelliferae

Main chemical components
● Acetic Acid, Aliphatic Aldehyde, Carotol, Daucol, Asanona, Beta-Carotene, Cineol, Formic Acid, Limonene, and Terpineol.

Did you know…?
● *There is also a carrier oil with a carrot base that is rich in vitamin A. However, it should constitute no more than ten percent of the total when preparing massage oil because it can turn skin slightly yellow, albeit temporarily.*

Therapeutic properties of the essential oil

- Antioxidant
- Antiparasitic
- Antirheumatic
- Antiseptic
- Carminative
- Cytophylactic
- Depurative
- Diuretic
- Emenagogue
- Gentle muscle relaxer
- Hepatic
- Orexigenic
- Stimulant
- Tonic
- Vasodilator

Advisory
● *This essential oil is very gentle and poses no risk of toxicity, sensitization or irritation of the skin. An emmenagogue, it is better not to use it during pregnancy so as not to affect the uterus or hormonal cycle.*

Therapeutic applications
● Amenorrhea, Anemia, Anorexia, Arthritis, Cramps, Spider Veins, Dermatitis, Hormonal Imbalance, Dysmenorrhea, Eczema, Edema, Gout, Indigestion, Intestinal Parasites, Psoriasis, Rheumatism, Pre-menstrual Syndrome, Blood Toxins, Urticaria.

Cosmetic applications
● Since it revitalizes and tones, this essential oil is a great ally of mature skin and wrinkles, for which it gives very good results.

Cedar

Latin name:
Cedrus atlantica
and *Juniper virginiana*

Family
Coniferae

General description

What is known as "cedar essential oil" comes from two different species of trees. The Atlas Cedar, the most authentic and which grows in Morocco, is related to the cedar of Lebanon, of which very few examples exist.

The essential oil of this conifer is pale yellow and its woody aroma is sweet and fragrant, reminiscent of sandalwood.

The Red Cedar of Virginia grows in North America and has a woody aroma. Dense and colorless, it has practically the same therapeutic applications as the Atlas Cedar.

The essential oil of this perennial evergreen tree that can reach heights up to 35 m. is obtained from the wood. It is extracted through steam distillation. Small quantities of resinoid and absolute can also be extracted from it.

Did you know...?
● *Cedar essential oil could be the first oil mankind extracted from a plant. There is evidence that it was used by the Egyptians to mummify their pharaohs and to build sarcophagi.*

Main chemical components
● Atlas Cedar: Cedrol, Cadinene, Cedrene, and Cedrenol
● Red Cedar of Virginia: Cedrol, Cadinene, Cedrenol, and Thujone

Therapeutic applications
● Arthritis, Bronchitis, Cystitis, Respiratory Congestion, Depression, Dermatitis, Eczema, Skin Rashes, Stress, Leucorrhea, Vaginal Itching, Psoriasis, Insect Repellent, Colds, Rheumatism, Sinusitis, Fear, Nervous Tension, Cough, Ulcers

Cosmetic applications

● The essential oil of cedar is very effective in the treatment of oily skin and acne. It also works well on scalps for dry hair, dandruff, and alopecia.

● In addition, it is used for anti-cellulite treatments because it stimulates lymphatic drainage and helps to eliminate fats. These benefits accompany its diuretic effect, which helps fight fluid retention and reduces cellulite.

Therapeutic properties of the essential oil

● Abortifacient	stimulant
● Antidepressant	● Diuretic
● Antispasmodic	● Emollient
● Antiputrefactive	● Expectorant
● Antiseborrheic	● Fungicide
● Antiseptic	● Insecticide
● Aphrodisíac	● Mucolític
● Astringent	● Sedative
● Balsamic	● Tonic
● Circulatory	

Celery

Latin name:

Apium graveolens
L. var. dulce

Family:

Apiaceae

General description

Essential oil can be extracted from either the wild celery plant or sweet celery. In its wild form, the leaf and stem have a strong disagreeable smell: the sweet variety found today at the vegetable stands has been bred to mitigate this odor. Wild celery has long been known, growing especially well in wetlands of the temperate climate of Europe.

Although all parts of the plant contain essential oil, the most popular type is extracted from the seed. It is soft yellow, with a very smooth texture, and has an intense aroma of celery.

Main chemical components

● Limonene, Selinene, Sedanolide, Sedanolide, Palmitic Acid, Apiol, Beta-terpineol

Did you know...?

● *In antiquity the Greeks called it "Plant of the Moon" (Selinon) and claimed that it acted on the nervous system, in addition to being a great tonic. Later, diuretic properties were attributed to it. The Romans also knew this plant, but gave it a different therapeutic application: they wore a crown made of it so as to better withstand hangovers.*

Therapeutic properties of the essential oil

● Antioxidant
● Antipigmentary
● Antispasmodic
● Bactericide
● Carminative
● Cholagogue
● Digestive
● Digestive tonic
● Diuretic
● Emenagogue

● Galactagogue
● Hepatic
● Nervine
● Orexigenic
● Sedative
● Venous Decongestant
● Urinary antiseptic
● Urinary stimulant

Advisory
● *Do not use if you are pregnant.*

Therapeutic applications
● Aphrodisiac, Amenorrhea, Anxiety, Arthritis, Fatigue, Kidney Stones, Sciatica, Cystitis, Liver Congestion, Blood Purification, Diabetes, Dyspepsia, Flatulence, Gout, Hemorrhoids, Stimulation of Milk Flow, Indigestion, Glandular Problems, Fluid Retention, Rheumatism.

Cosmetic applications
● It has been used in the treatment of pigment spots.

Ceylon Cinnamon

Latin name:

Cinnamomum zeylanicum

Family:

Lauracea

General description

This variety is the most prized of all cinnamons and comes, as the name suggests, from Ceylon, now Sri Lanka. A perennial tree, it belongs to the same family as laurel. It has glossy, oval leaves and clusters of small yellow flowers.

The essential oil is extracted from the leaves by distillation and can have a color ranging from yellow to brown. Its aroma is very spicy and warm, very similar to that of the spice used in cooking.

Main chemical components

● Cinnamic Aldehyde, Eugenol, Caryophyllin, Cymene, Linalool, Methyl Ketone, Phellandrene and Pinene.

Did you know...?

● *Aphrodisiac properties have always been ascribed to cinnamon. In his* Natural History *Pliny warned about women who used it to scent bed linens.*

Therapeutic properties of the essential oil

● Anthelmintic
● Antibacterial
● Antispasmodic
● Antiviral
● Aphrodisiac
● Astringent
● Cardiotonic

● Carminative
● Circulatory tonic
● Digestive
● Emenagogue
● Fungicide
● Hemostatic

Therapeutic applications

● Amenorrhea, Anorexia, Diarrhea, Dyspepsia, Intestinal Spasms, Stress, Nervous Exhaustion, Frigidity, Gingivitis, Flu, Functional Impotence, Dental Infections, Stomach Infections, Leukorrhea, Poor Circulation, Colds.

Cosmetic applications

● In cosmetics cinnamon oil is used in small doses as a firming agent for the skin; it is always mixed with other essential oils and a carrier oil.

● Cinnamon is part of many men's fragrances and its slightly astringent properties give good results in aftershave lotions.

Advisory

● *This oil is contraindicated during pregnancy and should always be applied diluted to 1%, because if applied directly to skin or in the bath water, it can cause major skin irritations.*

● *Although it has great therapeutic properties, you should never use this essential oil on its own, as it can be very irritating. It should always be prescribed by a specialist, due to a high content of Eugenol.*

Chamomile, German (or common) and Roman

Latin name:

Matricaria chamomilla and *Anthemis nobilis*

Family:

Asteraceae

General description

General description

Many species of chamomile grow in Europe, Africa, and Asia, but German, or common chamomile, and Roman, or noble, chamomile are the ones used in aromatherapy. Although their chemotypes differ slightly, they have nearly the same therapeutic applications and for that reason they are grouped together in this section. You can get one or the other (or even both) from all distributors of essential oils without any problem, since they are often used in aromatherapy for physical, emotional, or psychic ailments, and for cosmetic treatments.

Chamomile is part of the traditional medicine of many cultures. A plant with hairy stems and divided leaves, chamomile grows in temperate climates. Its flower is much like a daisy, and it is no coincidence that both are of the same family. It also has a yellow button in the center, but with tiny white petals and a very different aroma. It is in-

tense, fruity, and reminiscent of apple.

The essential oil is obtained by distillation from the dried flowers. Its color can range from a pale bluish hue to a deep blue in cases where there is a greater amount of azulene, a powerful anti-inflammatory active ingredient. The more it contains, the more viscous the texture and the richer the essential oil in therapeutic properties.

Main chemical components
- Azulene (not in the plant, but formed in the process of extracting the essential oil), Angelica, Borneol, Geraniol, Alpha-Bisabolol, Furfural,

Did you know…?
- *Roman chamomile has been used as a remedy in traditional European medicine for five centuries. Its name is derives from the belief that Romans cultivated it during the Renaissance. This plant does not grow spontaneously either in Italy or on the French Mediterranean coast.*

Methacrylic Acid, Sesquiterpene Alcohol, Caprylic acid, Monosilicic Acid

Therapeutic applications

● Allergy, Amenorrhea, Anemia, Arthritis, Asthma caused by stress, Bursitis, Urinary Calculus, Headache, Cystitis, Colic, Colitis, Conjunctivitis, Convulsions, Teething Pain (children), Depression, Inflammatory Dermatitis, Diarrhea, Dysmenorrhea, Dyspepsia, Eczema, Liver Fatigue, Fever caused by stress, Hay Fever, Flatulence, Boils, Gastralgia, Gastritis, Gingivitis, Gout, Halitosis, Hysteria, Jaundice, Loss of Appetite, Insomnia, Anger, Irritability, Menopause, Migraine, Nephritis, Facial Neuralgia, Otitis, Intestinal Parasites, Insect Bites, Vaginal Itching, Burns, Rheumatism, Chilblains, Sinusitis, Peptic Ulcer, External Ulcers, Urticaria, Vaginitis, Dizziness, Vomiting

Cosmetic applications

● The anti-inflammatory property of the azulene contained in chamomile essential oil is a big help for irritated and sensitive skin. In addition, its antiseptic property gives good results in cases of acne, abscesses, and boils.
● Blond hair is clearer after use of cosmetic

Advisory
● *Everyone can use chamomile essential oil without problems in all cases except if one is allergic to this plant.*

products containing this essential oil, and it is also used to combat dandruff or other hair problems such as seborrheic eczema.

Therapeutic properties of the essential oil

● Analgesic	● Antispasmodic	● Immunostimulant
● Antacid	● Bactericide	● Nerve sedative
● Anti-allergen	● Carminative	● Orexigenic
● Antianemic	● Cautery	● Splenic
● Anticonvulsive	● Cholagogue	● Stimulant
● Antidepressant	● Decongestant	● Sudorific
● Anti-inflammatory	● Digestive	● Tonic
● Antineuralgic	● Digestive tonic	● Vasoconstrictor (local)
● Antiparasitic	● Diuretic	● Vulnerary
● Antiphlogistic	● Emenagogue	
● Antirheumatic	● Febrifuge	
● Antiseptic	● Gastric stimulant	

Citronella

General description

This plant is related to lemongrass and palmarosa; it belongs to the family of tropical grasses. The most valued varieties come from Java, the Seychelles, New Guinea, Guyana, and Sri Lanka.

Its essential oil, which is extracted by distillation of the leaves, has a pronounced lemon scent and a hue that can vary from yellow to brown.

Latin name:
Cymbopogon nardus
Family
Gramineae

Main chemical components

● Although these vary according to the chemotype, Citroneol, Geraniol, Citral, Methyl Eugenol, and Borneol are usually present.

Therapeutic properties of the essential oil

- Antibacterial
- Anti-inflammatory
- Antipruritic
- Antirheumatic
- Antiseptic
- Antispasmodic
- Deodorant
- Diuretic
- Emenagogue
- Febrífuge
- Fungicide
- Insecticide
- Repels insects
- Stomachic
- Tonic

Advisory

● *Completely avoid it if you are pregnant because it helps regulate the menstrual cycle and may be abortifacient. For everyone else, it is not toxic or irritating, but it can cause allergic reactions in individuals sensitive to grasses..*

Therapeutic applications

● Headache, Mental Fatigue, Influenza, Insecticide, Migraine, Neuralgia, Insect Bites, Insect Repellent, Colds, Rheumatism, Menstrual Disorders

Cosmetic applications

● Due to its disinfectant and deodorizing properties, this oil is often found in soaps, insecticides and cleaning products.

Did you know...?

● *If you put a few drops on the sheets or near the pillow it can help you sleep without being bothered by mosquitoes. You can also rub the bites with a drop of citronella essential oil to relieve itching and inflammation and disinfect them at the same time. It should be diluted (10 drops of citronella essential oil in 25 ml. of sweet almond oil) if used on children under eight years old.*

Clary Sage (or Amaro)

General description

The clary sage is a large herbaceous plant with wrinkled leaves and a pink stem with purple flowers that have pointy petals and a waxy texture. It should be noted that it is very similar to common sage, but its flowers are much smaller. Used for thousands of years, its name comes from the Latin word "salvare," which means "to save," due to its reputation as a cure-all.

Amaro, or clary sage, is more often used in aromatherapy than common sage. Although they have similar properties, amaro oil is safer because it contains hardly any thujone.

The essential oil is extracted from the green part and the flowers by steam distillation. The fragrance is strong, dense, and clear. This essence is reminiscent of common sage, which is richer and more floral.

Latin name:
Salvia esclarea
Family:
Labiatae

Main chemical components
● Morneol, Camphor, Cineol, Pinene, Sclareol, Sclareolide, Linalyl Acetate, Caryophyllene.

Therapeutic applications
● Anxiety, Amenorrhea, Headache, Colic, Convulsions, Depression, Dysmenorrhea, Dyspepsia, Boils, Stress, Euphoria, Flatulence, Frigidity, Hypertension, Hysteria, Impotence, Throat Infections, Respiratory Infections, Leukorrhea, Menopause, Migraine, Neurastenia, Ophthalmia, Drowsiness, Pertussis, Nephritic Disorders, Ulcers.

Cosmetic applications
● This essential oil is often used in regenerative treatments to care for somewhat mature skins. It also is beneficial for oily skin and problems with acne.
● If you have oily hair or dandruff, clary sage can be used to regulate your scalp. In addition, it stimulates hair growth.

Did you know…?
● *In the age of the pharaohs it was believed that sage could cure infertility because it regulated menstruation. The Greeks and Romans were convinced that it promoted longevity.*

Therapeutic properties of the essential oil

- Analgesic
- Anticonvulsive
- Antidepressant
- Antispasmodic
- Anti-inflammatory
- Antiseptic
- Aphrodisiac
- Astringent
- Bactericide
- Balsamic
- Carminative
- Cautery
- Deodorant
- Digestive
- Emenagogue
- Hypotensive
- Nervine
- Sedative
- Stomachic
- Sudorífic
- Tonic
- Tonic during childbirth
- Uterine

Advisory

- *Although it should not be used during pregnancy, it is useful in the last stages of labor. Avoid it if you are breast-feeding your baby.*
- *It is advised not to use it when driving or operating machinery. Its sedative effect hinders concentration.*
- *High doses can cause headaches.*

Clove

General description

The clove tree grows in tropical countries, particularly on islands, as it tends to prefer coastal climates. Its height is less than 10 m. and its leaf is reminiscent of that of laurel, but of a lighter green with small brown spots that give off a spicy scent when crushed. The flowers are small and dark red, but not usually open; the spice is the bud of this tree.

Its great antiseptic property has made it a famous antiviral in many cultures. It was used to combat epidemics such as the plague. The essential oil is distilled from the flower buds and leaves, and the process should be carried out several times. Of a light but penetrating sweetish and spicy aroma, it is pale yellow when freshly distilled and darkens until it turns a brown hue as time passes.

Latin name:
Eugenia caryophyllata
Family:
Myrtaceae

Therapeutic properties of the essential oil

- Anesthetic
- Anthelmintic
- Antibiotic
- Antiemetic
- Antineuralgic
- Antioxidant
- Antiseptic
- Antiviral
- Carminative
- Expectorant
- Larvicide
- Orexigenic
- Spasmolytic
- Stimulant
- Stomachic
- Sedative

Main chemical components
- Eugenol, Acetyleugenol, Benzoic Acid, Benzyl Benzoate, Furfural, Beta-caryophyllene, and Vanillin.

Therapeutic applications
- Oral Thrush, Arthritis, Asthma, Bronchitis, Bursitis, Colic, Cuts, Denture Care, Diarrhea, Dyspepsia, Toothache, Flatulence, Frigidity, Flu, Halitosis, Anorexia, Nausea, Intestinal Parasites, Athlete's Foot, Gum Disease, Pneumonia, Insect Repellent, Colds, Rheumatism, Ulcers, Vomiting.

Cosmetic applications
- It is very useful in treatments to combat acne.

Did you know...?
- *If you are trying to quit smoking, sucking on cloves can help because it relaxes and soothes mental and physical stress, in addition to perfuming the breath.*

Advisory

• *Since it can cause mucous membrane irritation or dermatitis in sensitive skin, clove essential oil should always be used diluted to 1% at the most.*

Coriander (or cilantro)

General description

The coriander plant is distributed from China to Mexico and appears in the culinary traditions of many countries. With a very intense aroma, this perennial Umbelliferae has mauve flowers and dark green leaves that resemble those of parsley.

The essential oil, which is extracted by distillation of the seeds, has a yellowish tinge and a pleasant and powerful, spicy and musky scent.

Latin name:
Coriandrum sativum
Family:
Umbelliferae

Main chemical components
● Coriandrol, Geraniol, Pinene, Borneol, P-Cymene, Phellandrene, and Terpinene.

Therapeutic applications
● Anorexia, Arthritis, Diarrhea, Dyspepsia, Toothache, Muscle Aches, Facial Spasms, Muscle Spasms, Nervous Fatigue, Fever, Flatulence, Gout, Flu, Poor Circulation, Migraine, Nausea, Facial

Therapeutic properties of the essential oil

● Analgesic	● Febrífuge
● Antioxidant	● Fungicide
● Antirheumatic	● Larvicide
● Antispasmodic	● Lipolytic
● Aphrodisiac	● Orexigenic
● Bactericide	● Relaxant
● Carminative	● Stimulant
● Cytotoxic	● Stomachic
● Depurative	

Neuralgia, Colds, Fluid Retention, Rheumatism.

Cosmetic applications
● It has lipolytic properties that together with its depurative and cytotoxic power, helps eliminate fluid retention and cleanse the body of toxins. All of these benefits positively affect slimming treatments.
● It is also used in the composition of perfumes and in bath oils for women.

Did you know...?
● *In former times it was said that if a woman regularly ate coriander seeds, she could stop menstruating and get pregnant immediately.*

Cumin

Latin name:
Cuminus cyminum
Family
Umbelliferae

General description

The cumin plant is believed to be indigenous to Egypt, but it has grown in the Mediterranean basin for centuries. Of this umbelliferae, only the seed is used, both in herbal medicine and in aromatherapy. It is also a spice that is used in cooking, constituting one of the main ingredients in curry.

Although it resembles caraway and is reminiscent of anise, it is distinguished by the flavor. There is black cumin, which is highly prized, and white cumin, which is more common.

The oil is distilled from the seeds and is transparent, although over time it acquires certain shades of yellow-brown. Its aroma is very intense and very much like anise, but it is muskier.

Did you know...?
● *Cumin has been present in Mediterranean cultures for thousands of years; its seeds have been found in the tombs of the pharaohs of the Egyptian Empire.*

Advisory
● *This oil is photosensitizing, so you should not sunbathe after applying it in order to prevent hyperpigmentation of the skin.*

Therapeutic properties of the essential oil

- Antiseptic
- Antispasmodic
- Bactericide
- Carminative
- Laxative (gentle)
- Orexigenic
- Stimulates digestion

Main chemical components
● Cuminic Aldehyde, Cuminol, Cymene, Pinene, and Terpineol.

Therapeutic applications
● Aerophagia, Increases Male Fertility, Menstrual Cramps, Slow Digestion, Intestinal Spasms, Loss of Appetite, Slow Intestinal Transit.

Cosmetic applications
● Appears to be a good remedy for combating cellulitis. It is usually blended with orange or lemon essential oil to improve the aroma.

Cypress

Latin name:
Cupressus sempervivens
Family:
Cupressaceae

General description

This conifer, originating in the Mediterranean basin, was considered sacred by cultures such as that of Tibet or Egypt. According to tradition, Christ's cross was made of cypress wood.

Cypress is an evergreen tree with a conical crown that can reach up to 40 m. in height. The pale yellow-green essential oil is extracted by steam distillation from the branches, leaves, and cones. Its aroma is balsamic and lingers, leaving a fresh feeling in the atmosphere. It is ideal for helping the respiratory system, overcoming stress, and calming restless children.

Did you know...?

The Bathers (1877) Paul Cézanne

● *Cypress essential oil helps to regulate the female reproductive system and is one of the great allies of women in cases of menstrual disorders. In addition, its antiperspirant property helps to alleviate the hot flashes that accompany menopause.*

Main chemical components

● Beta-pinene, Terpineol, Cedrol, Cypress Camphor, Tannins, and Acids

Therapeutic applications

● Asthma, Bronchitis, Diarrhea, Dysentery, Dysmenorrhea, Edema, Enuresis, Bleeding, Hemorrhoids, Wounds, Stress, Flu, Impatience, Incontinence, Anger, Irritability, Poor Circulation, Menopause, Menorrhagia, Pyorrhea, Rheumatism, Nervous Tension, Spasmodic Cough, Whooping Cough, Liver Disorders, Varicose Veins

Cosmetic applications

● One of its cosmetic applications is as a deodorant. It is also a main ingredient in anti-cellulite treatments because it is a strong diuretic, astringent, and vasoconstrictor, which contributes considerably to decreasing fluid retention and improving circulation.
● It also helps to restore flexibility in tired skin and helps to regulate excessive sweating.

Therapeutic properties of the essential oil

- Antirheumatic
- Antiseptic
- Antispasmodic
- Antisudorífic
- Astringent
- Cautery
- Deodorant
- Diuretic
- Hemostatic
- Hepatic
- Insecticide
- Restorative
- Rebalances nerves
- Sedative
- Vasoconstrictor

Eucalyptus

Latin name:
Eucalyptus globulus and *other species*
Family:
Myrtaceae

General description

This tree is native to Australia, where it has long been used as a traditional remedy. It is now distributed worldwide and includes more than 600 species. In aromatherapy, *Eucalyptus globulus* is usually distilled to obtain the essential oil, although you can use dozens of other species that have similar active ingredients.

It is one of the tallest trees, and can reach a height of over 100 m. Of the species discussed here there are known to be examples that are 114 m. tall. Its evergreen leaves, oval and dark, contain the essential oil, and its bark exudes a gummy material with a balsamic odor.

The essential oil is very fluid and is distilled from the leaves and young branches. The best is obtained from trees that are already mature. Transparent with shades of pale yellow, its aroma is clean, pungent, balsamic, and very powerful. It is very useful for a wide range of physical ailments and emotional ones too. For example, it is very beneficial to place a few drops of eucalyptus essential oil in a diffusor in a room in which an argument has just occurred, as it helps to relax the atmosphere. It also calms the spirit and promotes concentration.

Main chemical components
● Eucalyptol, Citronella, Camphene, Eudesmol, Phellandrene, Pinene, and various alcohols

Therapeutic applications
● Blisters, Rheumatoid Arthritis, Asthma, Bronchitis, Gallstones, Calms the Spirit, Cystitis, Diabetes, Diarrhea, Diphtheria, Dyspepsia, Muscle Aches, Emphysema, Scarlet Fever, Promotes Concentration, Fever, Hay Fever, Typhoid, Gonorrhea, Flu, Bleeding, Wounds, Herpes, Throat Infections, Leukorrhea, Malaria, Migraine, Acute Nephritis, Neuralgia, Pediculosis (lice), Insect Bites, Burns, Insect Repellent, Colds, Rheumatism, Chilblains, Measles, Sinusitis, Cough, Tuberculosis, External Ulcers

Did you know…?
● *Surgeons used to clean surgical wounds with a solution of eucalyptus because of its strong antiseptic and antiviral properties.*
● *It is also very useful for disinfecting a patient's room, especially if in the case of a contagious disease.*

Advisory

● *The essential oil should be applied in dilution to avoid irritation. Not recommended for internal use, or for people with hypertension or epilepsy.*

● *Its balsamic properties can counteract the effects of homeopathic preparations, so both treatments should not be used simultaneously.*

Cosmetic applications

● It is effective in the treatment of scars and burns, in addition to clarifying clogged pores.

Therapeutic properties of the essential oil

● Analgesic	● Antiseptic	● Diuretic
● Anthelmintic	● Antiviral	● Expectorant
● Antispasmodic	● Bactericide	● Hypoglycemic
● Antiphlogistic	● Balsamic	● Insecticide
● Antineuralgic	● Cautery	● Rubefacient
● Antiparasitic	● Depurative	● Stimulant
● Antipyretic	● Decongestant	● Vulnerary
● Antirheumatic	● Deodorant	

Fennel

Latin name:
Foeniculum vulgare
Family:
Umbelliferae

General description

This dark green plant with feathery leaves can reach up to 2 m. in height. Its intense aroma makes it easy to identify, as do its yellow, umbrella-shaped flowers.

It is very common in the Mediterranean basin and has been present in many cultures around the world throughout the ages, both in the kitchen and in natural remedies for all kinds of diseases.

The essential oil is distilled from ground seeds. It is transparent but with tones of pale yellow. Its aroma is like anise, aromatic and spicy.

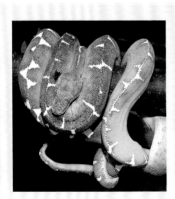

Did you know...?

● *In Asia great powers were attributed to fennel. One of the most prominent was its ability to neutralize all kinds of poisons, including snake venom. Far away from there, in Anglo-Saxon countries, it was considered one of the nine sacred herbs for warding off evil.*

Main chemical components
Anethole, Anisic Aldehyde, Camphene, D-fenchone, Dipentene, Estragole, Phellandrene, Phenone, and Pinene

Therapeutic applications

● Lung Conditions, Alcoholism, Amenorrhea, Anorexia, Antidote for Poisons, Asthma, Low Self Esteem, Bronchitis, Kidney Stones, Colic, Conjunctivitis, Dyspepsia, Low Milk Flow, Constipation, Flatulence, Gout, Hematomas, Hiccups, Menopause, Nausea, Obesity, Oliguria (low urine output), Gum Disease, Fluid Retention, Nervous Tension, Vomiting

Cosmetic applications

● Its natural estrogen content makes it a great ally of women who have premenstrual syndrome and menopause. It also facilitates weight loss as it helps to regulate metabolism and cleanse the body, a fact of which the ancient Greeks were well aware.

Advisory

● *We do not recommend the use of fennel essential oil during pregnancy because it contains natural estrogens.* ● *If applied in very high doses, it can produce a hypnotic effect on the patient; however, when used in moderation, there is no risk.*

Therapeutic properties of the essential oil

● Anthelminic	● Circulatory	● Galactogogue
● Antispasmodic	stimulant	● Laxative
● Anti-inflammatory	● Depurative	● Orexigenic
● Antimicrobial	● Detoxifier	● Splenic
● Antiphlogistic	● Diuretic	● Stomachic
● Antiseptic	● Emenagogue	● Sudorífic
● Carminative	● Expectorant	● Tonic

Geranium

Latin name:
*Pelargonium
graveloens*
Family:
Geraniaceae

General description

Geranium essential oil is one of the most important and versatile in aromatherapy. Cultivated in many countries, this plant does not exceed 60 cm. in height, and its leaves are green and toothed. The flowers can be many different colors, and the whole plant is aromatic. Therefore, the essential oil, obtained by distillation, is extracted from the stem, leaves, and flowers. Also, a concrete and an absolute can both be obtained. The essential oil has a greenish hue, although it is very transparent. Its intense aroma is floral, sweet and fresh, evocative of a rose, with a slight note of mint. It is very stimulating and lifts one's mood.

Main chemical components
● Geranic Acid, Borneol, Citral, Citroneol, Eugenol, Phellandrene, Geraniol, Linalool, Methone, Myrtenol, Pinene, Terpineol, and Sabinene.

Did you know…?
● *Planting geraniums on the balconies and windows of houses is an old tradition. It was believed that they could protect the home from evil spirits.*

Therapeutic applications
● Oral Thrush, Kidney Stones, Uterine Cancer, Broken Capillaries, Convalescence, Depression, Dermatitis, Diabetes, Diarrhea, Eczema, Infertility, Stomatitis, Stress, Fatigue, Stomach Pain, Glossitis, Hemorrhage, Hemorrhoids, Wounds, Herpes, Jaundice, Breast Congestion, Menopause, Facial Neuralgia, Ophthalmia, Pediculosis (lice), Athlete's Foot, Chilblains, Premenstrual Syndrome, Insect Repellent, Nervous Tension, Ringworm, Internal and External Ulcers.

Therapeutic properties of the essential oil

- ● Adrenal stimulant
- ● Analgesic
- ● Anthelminic
- ● Anticoagulant
- ● Antidepressant
- ● Anti-inflammatory
- ● Antiseptic
- ● Astringent
- ● Cautery
- ● Cytophylactic
- ● Deodorant
- ● Diuretic
- ● Hemostatic
- ● Hypoglycemic
- ● Insecticide
- ● Sedative
- ● Tonic
- ● Vasoconstrictor
- ● Vulnerary

Cosmetic applications

● It promotes cell regeneration, so it is used to treat mature or wrinkled skin. It also regulates the secretion of sebum in oily skin and hair with dandruff.

● Another of its properties is that it reactivates blood circulation, which brings a new vitality to dull complexions.

● It is also present in many anti-cellulite treatments as it stimulates the lymphatic system and helps remove liquids, in addition to reviving poor circulation. It is ideal for a refreshing and revitalizing bath in warm water, or total relaxation if the water is hot. It functions as a tonic and has a sedative effect on the nervous system.

Ginger

General description

The anthropomorphic rhizome of this perennial plant is of paramount importance in traditional Chinese medicine, where it is used frequently and for numerous ailments. Infinite virtues have been attributed to it, including its digestive benefits and not to mention its legendary properties as an aphrodisiac and aid to longevity.

In aromatherapy there are also many applications for its essential oil, its absolute, and its resinoid. These are the three substances that are extracted from the rhizome by steam distillation.

The intense aroma is warm and cool at the same time, spicy but pleasant. The color of the essential oil ranges from yellow to pale green to amber.

Latin name:
Zingiber officinale
Family:
Zingiberaceae

Therapeutic properties of the essential oil

- Analgesic
- Antiemetic
- Antiscorbutic
- Antispasmodic
- Antioxidant
- Antiseptic
- Antipyretic
- Aphrodisiac
- Carminative
- Cephalic
- Cough suppressant
- Euphoric
- Expectorant
- Laxative
- Orexigenic
- Rubefacient
- Stimulant
- Stomachic
- Sudorific
- Tonic

Advisory
- *It is phototoxic, so you should not sunbathe after applying it.*

Main chemical components
- Camphene, Citral, Cineole, D-Phellandrene, Isoborneol, Limonene Linalool, Resins, and Zingiberene.

Therapeutic applications
- Angina Pectoris, Arthritis, Cholesterol, Dyspepsia, Back Pain, Sore Throat, Toothache, Swelling, Sprains, Muscle Spasms, Fever, Bruising, Loss of Appetite, Malaria, Motion Sickness, Nausea, Colds, Rheumatism, Chilblains, Sinusitis, Sprains.

Did you know...?
Smelling a few drops of ginger essential oil on a handkerchief in the mornings before getting out of bed helps to overcome morning sickness characteristic of the early months of pregnancy.

Grapefruit

Latin name:
Citrus paradisi
Family:
Rutaceae

General description

The grapefruit is native to Asia, but apparently it was in the West Indies where it began to be cultivated in the eighteenth century. At present it is produced in places such as Brazil, Florida, Israel and, above all, California.

This citrus grows on trees with glossy leaves and white flowers. It is larger than an orange, and the yellow peel provides an essence with multiple therapeutic and cosmetic applications.

The essence, as with all citrus, is extracted by cold expression of the peel. It is very smooth and has a yellow-green tone. The aroma is intense and refreshing, acidic and sweet at the same time. It gives off a perfume that harmonizes one's surroundings and provides energy, stability, and optimism. It also cleans germs from the environment.

Did you know...?

● *Grapefruit essence has a magnificent effect on the atmosphere of your home or workplace. If you use it in a diffusor, it helps to purify and cleanse the air of negative energy, which helps to neutralize anxious or stressful situations. Its active ingredients balance the central nervous system, thus providing optimism, energy, and vitality.*

Main chemical components
● Citral, Linalool, Geraniol, Limonene, and Pinene.

Therapeutic applications
● Depression, Muscle Pain, Stress, Fatigue, Liver Fatigue, Nervous Fatigue, Flu, Loss of Appetite, Jet Lag, Migraine, Discomforts of Pregnancy, Abstinence Syndrome, Premenstrual Syndrome.

Cosmetic applications

● The active ingredients of grapefruit essence have multiple cosmetic applications. Since it promotes the elimination of liquids, it is used to combat cellulite. But it is also useful in cases of obesity. It is choleretic, which means that it stimulates the production of bile, and this helps the body to metabolize fats.

● Also, as an astringent, antiseptic, and antitoxic it stimulates the lymphatic system, which helps to treat congested, oily skin or acne problems with excellent results.

● It is also used to stimulate hair growth and to tone tired or mature skin.

Therapeutic properties of the essential oil

● Antidepressant	stimulant
● Antiseptic	● Disinfectant
● Antitoxic	● Diuretic
● Astringent	● Lymphatic
● Bactericide	stimulant
● Choleretic	● Orexigenic
● Depurative	● Revitalizer
● Digestive	● Tonic

Advisory

● *Do not use if you are pregnant.*

Hyssop

Latin name:
Hyssopus officinalis
Family:
Labiatae

General description

This is a bushy plant that does not exceed 60 cm. in height. It is native to southern Europe but now is grown and cultivated worldwide.

Its dark green leaves are narrow. Its blue, white or pink flowers are very aromatic and beloved by butterflies and bees.

The essential oil is distilled from the leaves and flowers. Of a golden yellow hue, its scent readily identifiable, and, although evocative of many other floral scents, the truth is that it is like no other.

Main chemical components
- Pinocamphone, Alcohol, Geraniol, Borneol, Thujone, and Phellandrene.

Did you know…?
In the pagan rites of ancient times, the faithful were purified with water sprays made with sprigs of hyssop. According to the Old Testament, it was one of the bitter herbs to be eaten during the Passover ritual.

Therapeutic properties of the essential oil

- Anthelminic
- Antispasmodic
- Antiseptic
- Astringent
- Antiviral
- Bactericide
- Balances blood pressure
- Carminative
- Cephalic
- Cautery
- Digestive
- Diuretic
- Emenagogue
- Expectorant
- Febrífuge
- Nervine
- Sedative
- Sudorífic
- Tonic cardiac
- Tonic pulmonary
- Vulnerary

Therapeutic applications
- Amenorrhea, Tonsillitis, Anxiety, Asthma, Bronchitis, Urinary Calculus, Colic, Bruises, Dermatitis, Dyspnea, Dyspepsia, Eczema, Scrofula, Stress, Nervous Fatigue, Fever, Flatulence, Flu, Wounds, Hypertension, Hypotension, Hysteria, Lack of Appetite, Leukorrhea, Otitis, Colds, Rheumatism, Syphilis, Nervous Tension, Cough, Whooping Cough, Tuberculosis

Cosmetic applications
- It is one of the oils most used in the manufacture of soaps.

Incense (or Frankincense)

General description

Incense is an oleoresin that comes from a shrub of the same name. For more than five millennia countless cultures have used it for a variety of ailments and for spiritual inspiration.

It is also called "frankincense". The shrub, native to Africa and the Middle East, is a relative of myrrh, another tree that produces oleoresin. Frankincense came to be as valuable as gold and is still used as an offering in Catholic masses, recalling the gift that the Magi brought to Jesus at His birth. The essential oil is not extracted from the leaves and flowers of this shrub but exclusively from the oleoresin secreted by its bark. Very pale in tone, it may be yellow or green. Its aroma, intense and with bass notes, evokes lemon, but it is much warmer and sensual.

Latin name:
Boswellia carteri
Family:
Burseráceas

Did you know…?

● *If you have asthma, it is useful to inhale a few drops of frankincense essential oil on a handkerchief, because it clears the air passages. In addition, its relaxing power will help asthmatic attacks, as it facilitates calm and rhythmic breathing.*

Main chemical components
● Acetone Alcohol, Resinous Materials, Camphene, Dipentene, Alpha-pinene, Beta-pinene, and Phellandrene.

Advisory

● *This essential oil does not irritate or sensitize the skin and, in addition, is an excellent vehicle for meditation and prayer, since its active ingredients enhance spiritual awareness.*

Cosmetic applications

● Its astringent properties make it a great ally for oily skin, but it also gives excellent results to dry, mature skin and problems with wrinkles, because it doubles as a regenerator and a tonic.

● It is also helpful in clearing up scars and blemishes associated with acne.

Therapeutic applications

● Anxiety, Asthma, Bronchitis, Anthrax or Malignant Anthrax, Cystitis, Dermatitis, Dysmenorrhea, Dyspepsia, Scrofula, Spermatorrhea, Stress, Gonorrhea, Gout, Flu, Bleeding, Wounds, Hyperventilation, Laryngitis, Leukorrhea, Metrorrhagia, Colds, Nervous Tension, Cough, Ulcers

Therapeutic properties of the essential oil

● Anti-inflammatory	● Digestive
● Antiseptic	● Diuretic
● Astringent	● Emenagogue
● Carminative	● Expectorant
● Cautery	● Sedative
● Cytophylactic	● Tonic
● Decongestant	● Vulnerary

Jasmine

Latin name:
Jasminum officinale
Family:
Oleaceae

General description

Jasmine essential oil is one of the most expensive in the world and acts mainly on an emotional level, so it is useful for overcoming psychological and psychosomatic problems. It is extracted from the flowers of a shrub and vine that grow throughout the Mediterranean basin and in China. Its leaves are bright green, and the star-shaped flowers, which can be white or yellow, release their penetrating aroma only at night. The essential oil is extracted with volatile solvents, although formerly the method of enfleurage was used, because flowers could not be subjected to the high temperatures of steam distillation. Afterwards a concrete and an absolute can be discerned by distillation.

Since the process is very delicate and requires a large amount of raw material, jasmine essential oil is very expensive. The tone of the absolute is a dark orange, but with a somewhat viscous liquid consistency. The perfume, of course, is sweet, dense, persistent, exotic, and very floral.

Main chemical components

● Acetate Benzyl, Linalyl Acetate, Benzyl Alcohol, Alpha-Terpineol, Methyl Antranilato, Geraniol, Indole, Jasmonate, and Linalool.

Therapeutic applications

● Aphonia, Anxiety, Depression, Dysmenorrhea, Nervous Chills, Muscle Spasms, Stress, Nervous Exhaustion, Frigidity, Impotence, Laryngitis, Colds, Coughs, Uterine Disorders.

Cosmetic applications

● It is very suitable for sensitive and irritated skin and is also recommended for dry skin on account of its emollient action on fats, and its antiseptic property.

Did you know...?
● *Jasmine essential oil helps restore self-confidence; it has a stimulating effect that leads to optimism, energy, and vitality. Apply it during a massage with the aid of a carrier oil. If you want to enhance the effect, combine jasmine with bergamot, geranium, and sandalwood.*

Advisory

● *If you are pregnant, you should be aware that the jasmine essential oil is a powerful tool for alleviating the pain of childbirth and for overcoming postpartum depression. However, do not use it until contractions have begun, because it can provoke premature birth.*

Therapeutic properties of the essential oil

- ● Analgesic
- ● Antidepressant
- ● Antispasmodic
- ● Anti-inflammatory
- ● Antiseptic
- ● Aphrodisiac
- ● Carminative
- ● Cautery
- ● Emolient
- ● Expectorant
- ● Galactagogue
- ● Obstetric
- ● Sedative
- ● Uterine tonic

Therapeutic properties of the essential oil

- Antiparasitic (external)
- Antihreumatic
- Antiseptic
- Antispasmodic
- Antitoxic
- Aphrodisíac
- Astringent
- Carminative
- Cautery
- Depurative
- Diuretic
- Emenagogue
- Nervine
- Rubefacient
- Sedative
- Stomachic
- Sudorífic
- Tonic
- Vulnerary

Juniper

General description

This perennial shrub continually produces berries. It grows throughout the northern hemisphere, but its essential oil improves the further south the plant is found. Its leaves are short, sharp-pointed, and joined in whorls of three.

Juniper is dioecious, meaning that it can be either male or female. Flowers grow on both, but berries are fruit born of the female. They are green and turn black when they when mature. The oil is extracted from the berries by steam distillation. It has a smooth texture and is transparent with a greenish-yellow glow. The aroma is reminiscent of pine.

Latin name:
Juniperus communis
Family:
Cupressaceae

Main chemical components

● Alpha-pinene, Borneol, Cadinene, Camphene, Caryophyllene, Camphor, Isoborneol, Juniperina, Terpene Alcohol, and Terpineol.

Did you know...?

● *In 1870 juniper wood was burned in French hospitals to combat an epidemic of smallpox. It has been used throughout history, beginning in prehistoric times, through to the Egyptians, Greeks, Romans, Middle Ages, Renaissance, and up to the contemporary period.*

Advisory

● *You should never use this oil if you are pregnant because it stimulates the uterine muscles and could provoke a miscarriage.*
● *You should not use this if you suffer from kidney disease. It is not recommended for children.*

Therapeutic applications

● Accumulation of Toxins, Albuminuria, Amenorrhea, Arteriosclerosis, Gonorrhea, Kidney Stones, Sciatica, Cirrhosis, Cystitis, Colic, Dermatitis, Diabetes, Dysmenorrhea, Dyspepsia, Eczema, Strangury (painful urination), Stress, Flatulence, Gout, Flu, Hemorrhoids, Wounds , Dropsy, Urinary Tract Infections, Pulmonary Infections, Leukorrhea, Lumbago, Oliguria (low urination), Pediculosis (lice), Chronic Pyelitis, Colds, Rheumatism, Cough, Nervous Disorders.

Cosmetic applications

● This essential oil is very useful for treating oily skin and problems with seborrhea and acne. It also works well for alopecia.
● It is also used in treatments for obesity and cellulite since it is diuretic and eliminates toxins and is also rubefacient and sudorific. Using it improves circulation and reduces fluid retention.

Key Lime

Latin name:
Citrus aurantifolia
Family:
Rutaceae

General description

The Key Lime tree does not exceed 5 m. in height and has evergreen leaves that are bright green. Its flower is small and white. The tree produces the key lime, a bright green fruit in the shape of a small lemon. Its bitter taste is very rich in vitamin C; Spanish and Portuguese sailors always carried it on board to avoid contracting scurvy.

Since it is a citrus essence, it is extracted from the peel by the cold expression method. Its color is very pale yellow or green, and the scent is fresh, sweet, and intense. It is impossible to forget the unique aroma of this fruit.

Main chemical components
- Linalool, Terpineol, Citral, Linalyl Acetate, Bergapten, Limonene, Pinene, Sabinene, and Terpinolene.

Did you know…?
- *Key lime is native to Asia and was brought to Spain by the Arabs. After that it was the Portuguese navigators and sixteenth-century Spaniards who introduced it in America, where it is grown mainly in the United States and Mexico.*

Therapeutic properties of the essential oil

- Analgesic
- Antidepressant
- Antiscorbutic
- Antimicrobial
- Antioxidant
- Antipyretic
- Antirrheumatic
- Antiseptic
- Antiviral
- Astringent
- Bactericide
- Carminative
- Disinfectant
- Deodorant
- Galactagogue
- Hemostatic
- Insecticide
- Nerve sedative
- Orexigenic
- Restorative
- Tonic

Therapeutic applications
- Heartburn, Oral Thrush, Alcoholism, Tonsillitis, Anemia, Anxiety, Apathy, Asthma, Bronchitis, Convalescence, Depression, Scurvy, Mental Fatigue, Fever, Boils, Wounds (small hemorrhage), Herpes, Hypertension, Indigestion, Poor Circulation, Nausea, Insect Bites, Colds, Rheumatism, Sinusitis, Cough and Varicose Veins.

Cosmetic applications
- Oily skin or acne problems can be significantly regulated and toned with key lime essence. It is very beneficial for strengthening brittle nails. It is often incorporated into treatments for cellulite and excess weight.

Advisory

● Key lime has phototoxic properties. It can cause skin spots if you sunbathe after applying massage oil that contains key lime. If you have very sensitive skin, use this essence in moderation because it can cause irritation.

Laurel

Latin name:
Laurus nobilis
Family:
Lauraceae

General description

This shrub, which can reach the height of a tree, has been considered by classical cultures as a symbol of elegance and triumph. But it is also recognized for its numerous culinary and thera-peutic properties.

Originally from Asia Minor, it is an evergreen shrub with smooth grey bark and long, sturdy, dark green leaves. The plants are unisexual, and the female shrubs are the ones that bear fruit. It is now grown everywhere and is a plant whose leaves are used routinely in many cuisines, espe-cially in the Mediterranean.

It also works well on an emotional level be-cause it gives energy to the body and the soul and enhances self-esteem. Its essential oil, which is distilled from the leaves, has a greenish yellow color and a pleasant aroma evocative of cajeput.

Therapeutic properties of the essential oil

- Analgesic
- Anticoagulant
- Antispasmodic
- Anti-infective
- Antiviral
- Bactericide
- Carminative
- Diuretic
- Emenagogue
- Expectorant
- Fungicide
- Mucolytic
- Sudorífic
- Vasoconstrictor

Main chemical components
- Cineol, Linalool, Alpha-Pinene, Eugenol, Geraniol, Phellandrene, Sesquiterpene, and Sesquiterpene Alcohol.

Therapeutic applications
- Aphonia, Arthritis, Asthma, Bronchitis, Bursitis, Dyspepsia, Fever, Flatulence, Flu, Hemorrhoids, Viral Infections, Pediculosis (lice), Scabies, Rheumatism, Stiff Neck, Menstrual Disorders.

Cosmetic applications
- This is strongly indicated for cases of oily skin or problems with acne, and also for dry scalps with hair loss. Since ancient times, a laurel-based hair tonic has been used to promote hair growth. It can also be used to lengthen eyelashes.

Did you know…?
- *Its Greek name recalls the nymph Daphne, who asked Zeus to change her into laurel to save her from being persecuted by Apollo. Since then it has been considered a plant of the gods.*

Apollo and Daphne (1681) by Carlo Maratti.

Advisory

● *You must not confuse* Laurus nobilis *with* Prunus laurocerasus. *The former is the authentic laurel; the latter is an ornamental cherry, sometimes called "common laurel." The former is the one that has therapeutic and cosmetic properties;* Prunus *can be poisonous because the leaves contain small quantities of prussic acid.*

Lavender

Latin name:
*Lavandula offici-
nalis* or *Lavandula
angustifolia*
Family:
Labiadas

General description

Lavender grows mainly in the Mediterranean basin. It is a perennial and has long, narrow, silvery-green leaves. The flowers range from deep mauve to grayish blue and are borne on top of long stems that grow from the center of the plant. Its aroma lies in small glands located on tiny hairs throughout the leaves, flowers, and stems. Simply touching the plant releases it, but it evaporates quickly because it is very volatile.

The essential oil is extracted from the flowers through the process of steam distillation. As with any essential oil from flowers, a large quantity of raw material is needed. In this case, you get a very intense aroma and a color ranging from dark yellow to dark greenish yellow. It is an essential oil that contains very many active ingredients. Its outstanding property is its ability to restore balance to all systems of the body, making it the

main ingredient of many aromatherapy preparations. The chemotype of the oil may differ depending on which part of the lavender from which it is extracted. In this sense, the French variety is the best quality, because it has a high content of linalyl acetate. This produces a floral aroma, fruity, sweet and rose-like. This plant has been nicknamed "Queen of Provence" because France, and this region in particular, is the largest producer of cultivated lavender.

Did you know…?

● *Lavender is also very useful for combating and repelling moths in your closet. This gives your clothes both protection and a pleasant aroma. In former times it was the most common way to perfume armoires. Furthermore, it is a good remedy to rid your dog or cat of parasites.*

Advisory

● *Although it has a very wide range of applications, this essential oil is very mild and can be used during pregnancy without problems. It can also be used on children.*

Main chemical components

● Borneol, Geraniol, Lavandulol, Linalool, Geranyl, Linalyl, Lavandulyl, Cineol, Caryophyllene, Pinene, Limonene, and Phenol.

Therapeutic applications

● Abscesses, Alopecia Areata, Anemia, Anxiety, Arthritis, Asthma, Blepharitis, Blennorrhagia, Bronchitis, Gallstones, Carbuncles, Headache, Cystitis, Hypochromic Anemia, Colic, Conjunctivitis, Convulsions, Depression, Dermatitis, Dizziness, Diarrhea, Diphtheria, Dyspepsia, Eczema, Edema, Epilepsy, Scrofula, Stress, Fatigue, Hay Fever, Typhoid Fever, Fistula, Flatulence, Boils, Gonorrhea, Gout, Flu, Halitosis, Bruises, Wounds, Herpes, Hypertension, Hysteria, Throat Infections, Sunstroke, Insomnia, Anger, Laryngitis, Leucorrhea, Menopause, Migraine, Nausea, Neurasthenia, Oliguria (low urination), Otitis, Palpitations, Paralysis, Pediculosis (lice), Insect Bites, Athlete's Foot, Psoriasis, Burns, Colds, Rheumatism, Chilblains, Scabies, Nervous Tension, Cough, Whooping Cough, Tuberculosis, Cutaneous Ulcers, Corneal Ulcers, Hives and Vomiting

Therapeutic properties of the essential oil

● Analgesic	● Carminative	● Fungicide
● Anticonvulsive	● Cautery	● Hypotensive
● Antidepressant	● Cytophylactic	● Insecticide
● Antispasmodic	● Cholagogue	● Nervine
● Antiphlogistic	● Choleretic	● Restorative
● Antimicrobial	● Decongestant	● Rubefacient
● Antiparasitic	● Deodorant	● Sedative
● Antirheumatic	● Detoxifier	● Splenic
● Antiseptic	● Diuretic	● Tonic
● Antioxidant	● Emenagogue	● Vulnerary

Cosmetic applications

● Lavender is a great wildcard in cosmetics because it relaxes, invigorates, increases tissue elasticity, helps heal and regenerate the cells, decongests tired complexions, and repairs skin that is sensitive or allergic.

● Since it stimulates cell growth and regulates excess fat, it is also useful for combating cellulite.

● For the same reason, it is highly recommended for cases of acne, oily skin, or dandruff. It also gives good results for alopecia caused by stress.

● Its great power as a relaxant mitigates the havoc wreaked by stress on our bodies and skin. A hot bath with a few drops of lavender essential oil at the end of the day can work wonders.

Lemon

Latin name:
Citrus limon
Family:
Rutaceae

General description

The lemon tree is a scented evergreen fruit tree that has bright green, pink and white flowers and bright yellow, oval fruits with an acid and pungent aroma. This citrus was known to cultures such as the Egyptian or Persian, as well as the Greek and Roman.

Today there are a great many varieties, and several chemotyes can be found in aromatherapy.

The essential oil is obtained by expression (also called "crushing") of the peel, as is the case with all citrus. It is actually an essence, because it has not undergone any alteration by temperature or solvents, which happens with other methods of extraction. As a result, it is a major source of vitamin C and other beneficial active ingredients, although its shelf life is relatively short. Its color can range from yellow to green, and its aroma is very intense, yet cool and pleasant.

Did you know…?

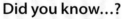
● *Until recently, in France lemon essential oil was regarded as a "cure-all" and was used for numerous indications. In addition, it was used as an antiseptic and disinfectant in Gallic hospitals until the First World War.*

Main chemical components

● Linalool, Citral, Citronellol, Cadinene, Bisabolene, Camphene, Dipentene, Limonene, Phellandrene, Pinene, Bergamottin, and Diosmin.

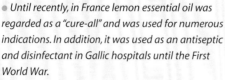

Cosmetic applications

● Lemon essential oil has many uses in cosmetics, especially as a clarifier and cleanser. Therefore it is often used for oily skin with blemishes or acne problems, and for all skin types to clean them deeply and remove dead cells.

● It can also be applied to the scalp to treat dandruff.

● In addition, it is used in treatments for obesity on account of its laxative and cleansing properties, and because it promotes microcirculation, which prevents the formation of cellulite. It is also a good treatment for brittle nails.

Therapeutic applications

● Heartburn, Anemia, Anxiety, Apathy, Arteriosclerosis, Arthritis, Bronchitis, Corns, Conjunctivitis, Depression, Slow Digestion, Dyspepsia, Poisoning, Scurvy, Constipation, Stress, Fever, Gout, Nosebleeds, Hypertension, Increased Concentration, Malaria, Poor Circulation, Immune System Booster, Psoriasis, Insect Repellent, Colds, Rheumatism, Premenstrual Syndrome, Typhoid, Cough, Ulcers, Varicose Veins, Warts.

Therapeutic properties of the essential oil

● Antianemic	● Anti-warts	● Hemostatic
● Antiesclerotic	● Astringent	● Hepatic
● Antiescorbutic	● Bactericide	● Hypoglycemic
● Antispasmodic	● Carminative	● Hypotensive
● Antimicrobial	● Cautery	● Insecticide
● Antineuralgic	● Depurative	● Laxativd
● Antipruritic	● Diaphoretic	● Rubefacient
● Antirheumatic	● Diuretic	● Stimulant
● Antiseptic	● Emolient	● Stomachic
● Antitoxic	● Febrifuge	● Tonic

Lemongrass

General description

Latin name:
Cymbopogon citratus
and *Cymbopogon flexuosus*
Family:
Poaceae
(Gramineae)

This plant, which until the middle of the last century was mainly grown in India, is an herb with long green and red leaves that are very aromatic. It grows very quickly and soon depletes the soil of nutrients and can easily reach 2 m. in height. Its essential oil is obtained from the leaves by steam distillation. It is a pale yellow and has an intense lemon and herbaceous aroma, hence the English name "lemongrass."

It has great antiseptic power and is very useful for purifying the atmosphere of a room in which someone with an infectious illness is convalescing or has convalesced, because it prevents infections caused by bacteria, which still lingers in the air.

Main chemical components
- Both varieties contain Citral, Neral, and Geranial.
- *Cymbopogon citratus*:
Caprylic, Citronellol, Dipentene, Farnesol, Furfural, Geraniol, Isopulegol, Isovaleric Aldehyde, Linalool, Methylheptane, Myrcene, N-Decyl Aldehyde, Nerol, Terpineol, and Valeric Esters.
- *Cymbopogon flexuosus*:
Citronellol, Dipentene, Farnesol, Geraniol, Limonene, Linalool, Methylheptane, Myrcene, N-Decyl Aldehyde, and Nerol.

Therapeutic applications
- Apathy, Headache, Cholera, Colitis, Convalescence, Dermatitis, Listlessness, Slow Digestion caused by stress, Sore Throat, Eczema, Stress, Nervous Fatigue, High Fever, Boils, Gastroenteritis, Gout, Indigestion, Infections, Jet Lag, Breast-feeding, Laryngitis, Small Infections, Pediculosis (lice), Athlete's Foot, Prevents the Development of Tumors, Insect Repellent, Moth Repellent, Parasite-Repellent for Pets, Chilblains, Excessive Sweating, Varicose Veins

Did you know…?
- *For thousands of years lemongrass has been a major ingredient in Thai cuisine, and in traditional Hindu medicine. On account of this it is also known as "Indian melissa oil" or "Indian verbena."*

Therapeutic properties of the essential oil

- Analgesic
- Antidepressant
- Antimicrobial
- Antioxidant
- Antipyretic
- Antiseptic
- Astringent
- Bactericide
- Carminative
- Deodorant

- Digestive
- Diuretic
- Febriguge
- Fungicide
- Galactagogue
- Insecticide
- Nervine
- Prophylactic
- Sedative
- Stimulant

Advisory

- *This essential oil can produce irritation in sensitive skin, so you should test it first on a small area.*

Cosmetic applications

- Lemongrass essential oil tones the skin, so it is usually present in the treatments that combat sagging skin caused by weight loss.
- In addition, it regulates excess fat in skin, greasy hair, and open pores. It also helps control excessive sweating, so it is a good deodorant.

Mahogany (or Rosewood)

General description

Latin name:
Aniba rosaeodora
Family:
Lauraceae

Also called "Rosewood," this is a tropical tree that grows wild in the Brazilian rainforest, where it is known as "jacaranda." It is evergreen with red bark and yellow flowers. The essential oil is fluid and pale yellow, extracted by distillation from the heartwood chips. The scent is very sweet, floral, and spicy with a soft, woody note. It recalls the rose but with wood in the background.

Main chemical components
● Geraniol, Linalool, Nerol, Terpineol, Cineole, Dipentene.

Therapeutic applications
● Fatigue, Weakness, Stress, Fever, Frigidity, Impotence, Immuno-suppression, Headache, Jet Lag, Meditation, Migraine with Nausea, Colds, Nervous Tension, Dry Cough

Did you know...?
● *Rosewood is also used to make furniture in the United States and chopsticks in Japan. Moreover, in France it is also used in construction and joinery.*

Advisory
● *Rosewood oil is extracted from a tree that grows in the Amazon jungle, and its overuse may be contributing to deforestation. Therefore, we must use it sparingly.*

Therapeutic properties of the essential oil

● **Analgesic**	● **Deodorant**
● **Anticonvulsive**	● **Immunologic**
● **Antidepressant**	**stimulant**
● **Antimicrobial**	● **Insecticide**
● **Antiseptic**	● **Mosquito repellent**
● **Aphrodisiac**	● **Sedative (gentle)**
● **Bactericide**	● **Tonic**
● **Cephalic**	

Cosmetic applications
● Rosewood is very effective in the care of dry, mature, or tired skin due to its regenerative properties, and as a cellular stimulant. There are those who argue that when combined with rose essential oil, it can even rejuvenate.
● It also helps skin that is dull, tender, or swollen, and with acne problems.

Advisory

● *Mandarin essential oil is phototoxic, so remember not to apply it on your skin if you are going to sunbathe.*

Mandarin

General description

This fruit tree is part of the same family as the orange tree, but its leaves and fruit are smaller, and its aroma is sweeter and more delicate. In addition, the skin does not adhere to the fruit, the sections of which are joined together.

It grows very well in warm climates, especially in Mediterranean types. Its essential oil is actually an essence, as is the case for all citrus, and is extracted from the peel by the expression method and does not undergo any alteration. It is a light yellow-orange and the aroma is almost floral, but with a hint of citrus, pointing to its origin. It is an essence that spoils quickly, so you should pay special attention to the date of purchase.

Latin name:
Citrus reticulata
Family:
Rutaceae

Main chemical components
- Limonene, Geraniol, Citral, Citronelol, and Methyl Anthranilate.

Did you know...?
- *This fruit was offered as a gift to the mandarins in ancient China as a symbol of respect, hence its name. It was not introduced to Europe until the beginning of the nineteenth century.*

Therapeutic properties of the essential oil

- Antiseptic
- Antispasmodic
- Carminative
- Cholagogue
- Cytophylactic
- Digestive
- Diuretic (gentle)
- Emolient
- Laxative (gentle)
- Lymphatic stimulant
- Sedative

Therapeutic applications
- Anxiety, Depression, Restlessness, Dyspepsia, Edema, Constipation, Stress, Liver Fatigue, Wounds, Hiccups, Poor Appetite, Indigestion, Insomnia, Irritability, Fluid Retention, Premenstrual Syndrome, Nervous Tension.

Cosmetic applications
- It is frequently used to treat oily and congested skin, blemishes, stretch marks and pimples.
- It also is beneficial in treatments for obesity because it helps to eliminate liquids and has a slight laxative effect.

Marjoram

Latin name:
Origanum majorana
Family:
Labiatae

General description

This very fragrant plant has reddish stems, dark green oval leaves, and small white, pink, or mauve flowers. It is found across southern Europe and northern Africa but is native to Asia. The essential oil is extracted by distillation using only the flowers, even though the stems and leaves are also very aromatic. For a short time after being extracted it is a greenish yellow, but it turns brown as time passes. Its scent is very distinctive, sweet and spicy at the same time, and evokes notes of camphor, thyme, pepper, and cardamom.

Main chemical components
• Carvacol, Thymol, Borneol, Camphor, Cineole, Cymene, Pinene, Sabinene, and Terpineol.

Did you know...?
This plant was considered sacred to the gods Vishnu, Siva and Osiris, it was used in Catholic convents for its anaphrodisiac property. However, the Greeks associated it with Aphrodite the goddess of fertility. Newly married couples were crowned with marjoram so that they would have good fortune in their marriage.

Therapeutic applications
• Anxiety, Arthritis, Asthma, Panic Attack, Bronchitis, Bursitis, Severe Headache, Colic, Depression, Sexual Desire, Diarrhea, Dysmenorrhea, Dyspepsia, Muscle Aches, Constipation, Stress, Bloating, Bruising, Hyperactivity, Hypertension, Hysteria, Insomnia, Headache, Leucorrhea, Lumbago, Poor Circulation, Dizziness, Migraine, Nausea, Neurasthenia, Colds, Chilblains, Premenstrual Syndrome, Sinusitis, Nervous Tension, Nervous Tics, Menstrual Disorders.

Cosmetic applications
● It has been used as an ingredient in cologne, to scent bath water, and as snuff.
● In cosmetics it is used together with other essential oils to prevent the appearance of stretch marks and to give elasticity to the skin.

Advisory
● *You should not use marjoram essential oil if you are pregnant. It is harmful to small children.*

Therapeutic properties of the essential oil

● Analgesic	● Diuretic
● Anaphrodisiac	● Emmenagogue
● Antioxidant	● Expectorant
● Antiseptic	● Fungicide
● Antispasmodic	● Hypertensive
● Antiviral	● Laxative
● Carminative	● Nervine Tonic
● Cephalic	● Sedative
● Cordial	● Vasodilator
● Diaphoretic	● Vulnerary
● Digestive	

Advisory
● *Melissa essential oil regulates the menstrual cycle, so you cannot use if you are pregnant, as it may provoke miscarriage.*

Melissa

General description

Melissa grows throughout the northern hemisphere, including Siberia, and in the temperate zone of the southern hemisphere. This perennial herb, also called "Lemon Balm," is very fragrant and has toothed dark green leaves and flowers that can be white, pink, or yellow.

Its essential oil is extracted from the leaves and flowers by distillation. It is pale yellow with a fresh lemon scent, clean and very intense. To obtain it requires a large quantity of raw materials, making it one of the most difficult to find in pure form, and usually very expensive.

Latin name:
Melissa officinalis
Family:
Labiatae

Main chemical components
● Citral, Citronellol, Geraniol, Geranyl Acetate, Caryophyllene, Citronellic Acid, Limonene, Linalool, and Pinene.

Therapeutic properties of the essential oil

● **Anthelmintic**	● **Febrifuge**
● **Antidepressant**	● **Fungicide**
● **Antihistamine**	● **Hypertensive**
● **Antispasmodic**	● **Nervine**
● **Bactericide**	● **Sedative**
● **Carminative**	● **Stimulant**
● **Cordial**	● **Stomachic**
● **Digestive**	● **Sudorific**
● **Emmenagogue**	● **Tonic**

Therapeutic applications
● Low Spirits, Allergies, Anxiety, Asthma, Panic Attacks, Colic, Depression, Dysentery, Eczema, Female-Sterility, Fever, Bleeding Wound, Hypertension, Hysteria, Indigestion, Insomnia, Headache, Melancholy, Migraine, Nausea, Palpitations, Insect Stings, Colds, Shock, Over Excitement, Nervous Tension, Chronic Cough, Menstrual Disorders, Grief, Dizziness, Vomiting.

Cosmetic applications
● Treatments for oily hair and alopecia containing melissa essential oil yield good results, and it is also recommended for cases of eczema or fungal infection.

Did you know…?
● *Melissa honey is one of the most appreciated and is said to have been what bees fed to Zeus when he was small. "Melittena" means "bee" in Greek, and the Greek nymph that protects this insect is called Melisa.*

Mint

Latin name:
Mentha piperita
Family:
Labiatae

General description

There are many varieties of mint, a plant that is grown in many parts of the world, although peppermint is native to the Mediterranean basin. The plant has square stems and small green leaves paired with flowers ranging from white to purple that grow in summer. The whole plant is very aromatic because odorous glands are spread throughout the stem and leaves. All you need to do is touch it with your fingers to release its fresh and unique fragrance into the atmosphere.

The essential oil is extracted from the leaves and flowers by distillation. When recently made it is transparent and very fluid, but over time it will thicken and darken.

Did you know...?

● *The name of this plant also is to be found, as in other cases, in Greek mythology. Mentha was a nymph for whom Pluto had an unbridled passion. Persephone, his jealous wife, chased her and trampled her to death. Then Pluto transformed his love into an aromatic plant that gave off a delicious scent every time someone pressed it or stepped on it.*

Main chemical components
● Menthol, Carvone, Cineole, Limonene, Menthone, Pinene, Thymol, and Valeric Acid.

Therapeutic applications
● Aerophagia, Canker Sores, Asthma, Bronchitis, Gallstones, Headaches, Sciatica, Cholera, Colic, Dermatitis, Dizziness, Diarrhea, Dysmenorrhea, Dyspepsia, Toothache, Muscle Pain, Stress, Mental Fatigue, Fever, Flatulence, Stomach Pain, Gingivitis, Flu, Halitosis, Bruising, Hysteria, Lack of Appetite, Indigestion, Motion Sickness, Migraine,

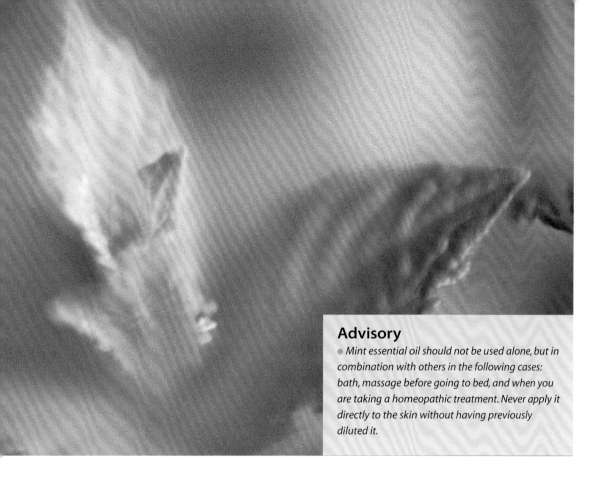

Nausea, Neuralgia, Palpitations, Paralysis, Tired Legs, Itching, Mosquito Repellent, Colds, Scabies, Shock, Sinusitis, Ringworm, Nervous Disorders, Tuberculosis, Dizziness, Vomiting.

Cosmetic applications

● Mint essential oil is used in various treatments for acne because it purifies the blood on account of its antiseptic and antibacterial properties.

● It is also used in shampoos for oily hair or dandruff and is a common ingredient in toothpaste, mouthwash, and massage cream for tired legs.

Therapeutic properties of the essential oil

- Analgesic
- Anthelmintic
- Anti-galactagogue
- Antiphlogistic
- Antiseptic
- Antispasmodic
- Antiviral
- Astringent
- Bactericide
- Carminative
- Cephalic
- Cordial
- Emmenagogue
- Febrifuge
- Hepatic
- Nervine
- Sudorific
- Vasoconstrictor

Myrrh

Latin name:
Commiphora myrrha
Family:
Burseraceae

General description

Used for over three thousand years by different cultures ranging from Chinese, Greek and Tibetan, the oleoresin of this shrub has been credited with miracles and sanctity. In the Bible, for example, it appears at the crucifixion of Christ, and it was one of the presents offered by the Magi to the Infant Jesus.

Originally from India, the Middle East, and northeastern Africa, this small tree, which does not exceed 10 m. in height, has aromatic leaves and tiny white flowers. However, its benefits come from its interior, the resin inside the trunk. This oleoresin is what undergoes steam distillation, resulting in an amber, sometimes reddish, essential oil with a warm, intense aroma.

Main chemical components
● Myrrholic Acid, Formic Acid, Acetic Acid, Palmitic Acid, Cinnamic Aldehyde, Cumic Aldehyde, Eugenol, Cadinene, Dipentene, Heerabolene, Limonene, and Pinene.

Cosmetic applications
● Its effectiveness in treating aging skin and wrinkles, has been known since ancient Egypt. It also gives good results for dry skin.

Advisory
● *You should not use this oil in high concentrations. It is contraindicated for pregnant women because it promotes contractions and regulates menstruation.*

Therapeutic applications
● Aphonia, Amenorrhea, Apathy, Arthritis, Asthma, Bronchitis, Chlorosis (iron deficiency anemia), Diarrhea, Dyspepsia, Sore Throat, Eczema, Stomatitis, Pharyngitis, Flatulence, Gingivitis, Hemorrhoids, Wounds, Hyperthyroidism, Anorexia, Nervousness, Athlete's foot, Gum Disease, Pruritus, Psoriasis, Colds, Rheumatism, Ringworm, Cough, Thrush, Cutaneous Ulcers.

Therapeutic properties of the essential oil

● **Cold remedy**	● **Emenagogue**
● **Antiphlogistic**	● **Expectorant**
● **Anti-inflammatory**	● **Fungicid**
● **Antimicrobial**	● **Sedative**
● **Antiseptic**	● **Stimulant**
● **Astringent**	● **Stomachic**
● **Balsamic**	● **Sudorífic**
● **Carminative**	● **Tonic**
● **Cautery**	● **Uterine**
● **Deodorant**	● **Vulnerary**

Vetiver

General description

The name of the plant comes from India, where it originated, and means "to rake," in other words to clean the ground. In that country it is grown to prevent soil from becoming eroded when the rains come. Tall, perennial and aromatic, it has a straight stem, long narrow leaves, and purple spikes that bend when the wind blows.

Its root is a white rhizome, from which, once dried and crumbled, the essential oil is extracted by distillation. The perfume industry also submits it to the volatile solvent method, which yields a resinoid present in many product ranges for men. The oil is, in contrast to the majority, very dark brown with a viscous texture that exudes a sensual, lingering essence, with a woody and earthy note, reminiscent of violets and sandalwood.

Latin name:
Vetiveria zizanoides and *Andropogon muricatus*
Family:
Gramineae

Advisory
● *It is an expensive oil, and you must always ensure that is pure and organic. In the 1970s many adulterations were sold, which gave it a reputation for having harmful effects on the skin. If you are sure of the source, there should be no problem when you use it, because in pure form it is not toxic and does not irritate or sensitize the skin.*

Therapeutic properties of the essential oil

- Anthelmintic
- Antispasmodic
- Antiseptic
- Aphrodisiac
- Circulatory and immune system stimulant
- Depurative
- Emenagogue
- Insectrepellent
- Nervine
- Rubefacient
- Sedative
- Tonic

Main chemical components
● Benzoic Acid, Vetiverol, Furfural, Vetivone, and Vetivene.

Therapeutic applications
● Exhaustion, Amenorrhea, Anxiety, Arthritis, Liver Congestion, Coronaritis, Weakness, Dependence on Tranquilizers, Depression, Muscle Pain, Enriches Blood, Sprains, Muscle Spasms (cramps), Mental Fatigue, Fever, Wounds, Immunosuppression, Sunstroke, Insomnia, Pancreatic insufficiency, Oligomenorrhea, Rheumatism, Moths, Nervous Tension, Severe Psychic Trauma, Urticaria

Cosmetic applications
● Its antiseptic and blood stimulating properties make it very suitable for the treatment of oily skin or acne problems.

Orange, bitter

General description

The bitter orange seems to be the origin of all citrus species we know today such as the sweet orange and mandarin, in addition to lemons, limes, grapefruits and other hybrids.

Brought by Arabs in the days of Andalusia, they are trees that do not exceed 10 m. in height, with evergreen foliage that is dark green, and white flowers from which neroli essential oil is extracted.

Bitter orange oil is extracted by cold expression of the peel. It is clear orange in color and, obviously, smells like an orange but with a more intense aroma than sweet oranges. However, because it has a short shelf life, it quickly turns brown and exudes an unpleasant odor, so it should be bought in small quantities.

Latin name:
Citrus aurantium
Family:
Rutaceae

Did you know…?
● *The bitter orange variety is mainly ornamental. In Andalusia, Seville and the surrounding area became a vast bitter orange grove.*

Therapeutic properties of the essential oil

- Antiemetic
- Anti-infective
- Antioxidant
- Cautery
- Cytophylactic
- Decongestant
- Digestive
- Orexigenic

Advisory
● *Like all citrus essences, the bitter orange is phototoxic, and you should not be exposed to sunlight after applying it to avoid sensitization and skin blemishes.*

Main chemical components
● Limonene, Citral, Citronellol, Geraniol, Linalool, Methyl Anthranilate, Nonyl Alcohol, and Terpineol.

Therapeutic applications
● Anorexia, Anxiety, Dyspepsia, Stress, Flatulence, Nervous Fatigue, Injury, Loss of Appetite, Skin Infections, Insomnia, Sinusitis, Vomiting

Cosmetic applications
● Since it promotes cell regeneration, it is a valuable aid to mature skin with wrinkles.

Orange Blossom (Neroli)

General description

Latin name:
Citrus aurantium
Family:
Rutaceae

Neroli is the name given to orange blossom essential oil, which is from the flower of the bitter orange. The Spanish name of the blossom stems from the Arabic word "al-azahar," which means "white flower." This flower is found primarily on the Mediterranean coast and regions with climates that are not extremely cold.

Neroli is named after the Italian Princess Ana Maria de Nerola, who used it to perfume her extensive collection of gloves. This seems to have really wreaked havoc on the men who approached her.

These flowers give rise to the bitter oranges on the ornamental trees that came from China and spread to the south of Spain.

Currently, neroli is widely used in perfumery, especially in those fragrances that are marketed as aphrodisiacs. Although the essential oil is extracted from flowers, their fleshy texture allows it to be distilled, which is why it is not too expensive. It is a beautiful pale yellow and has a penetrating floral aroma, fruity, sweet and sensual. It is surely one of the most exquisite and evocative that can be found.

In addition, with volatile solvents, one concrete and one absolute can be extracted from neroli. There are producers who still use the method of effleurage, which is much more laborious, but more natural than the former.

Main chemical components

● Phenylacetic Acid, Renol, Geraniol, Linalool, Nerolidol, Terpineol, Linalyl Acetate, Methyl Anthranilate, Neryl Acetate, Jasmone, Camphene, and Limonene.

Therapeutic applications

● Exhaustion, Chronic Anxiety, Apathy, Emotional Crises, Cuperosis, Depression, Diarrhea, Dysmenorrhea, Nervous Dyspepsia, Stress, Fatigue, Hysteria, Insomnia, Irritability, Headaches, Poor Circulation, Menopause, Neuralgia, Palpitations, Shock, Premenstrual Syndrome, Nervous Tension.

Did you know…?
● *Neroli essential oil was very popular in Venice, where it was thought to help combat plague and fevers.*

Therapeutic properties of the essential oil

- Aphrodisiac
- Antidepressant
- Antispasmodic
- Antiseptic
- Bactericide
- Cardíac tonic
- Carminative
- Cautery
- Circulatory tonic
- Cytophylactic
- Cordial
- Deodorant
- Digestive
- Emolient
- Nerve stimulant
- Euphoric
- Fungicide
- Hypnotic (gentle)
- Revitalizer

Advisory

● *There are no contraindications of any kind because it is a non-toxic essential oil that does not irritate or sensitize the skin. It can be used throughout pregnancy.*

Cosmetic applications

● It is a powerful ally of mature, sensitive, and dry skin, because it improves skin elasticity and helps regenerate cutaneous cells. It also helps with acne, stretch marks, and scars.

● In addition, it has been used for centuries in cosmetics, cologne, and scented baths.

Advisory
● *Like other essences from citrus, it is photosensitizing and you should not sunbathe after applying it to prevent irritation or skin blemishes.*
● *This oil can be used throughout pregnancy and can even be applied on young children, but always diluted in a carrier oil.*

Orange, sweet

General description

This fruit grows on a tree with evergreen leaves that are bright green. It belongs to a variety that is smaller than the bitter orange, another well known citrus that produces an essential oil with multiple applications.

The fruit has a sweet pulp, and the membranes between the segments are not bitter.

The essential oil is actually an essence, since it is extracted by the process of expression, namely by pressing the peel, and is not subjected to the effect of heat or solvents. So it's a natural product that spoils easily but maintains all the benefits of the fruit from which it comes. Its color is orange-yellow, and the fragrance is fruity, sweet, and intense.

Latin name:
Citrus sinensis
Family:
Rutaceae

Did you know…?
● *While the Arabs had already been familiar with the therapeutic properties of orange oil for thousands of years, Europe did not take advantage of it until the Renaissance. Then the orange was considered a luxury and was a much appreciated gift at Christmas time.*

Therapeutic properties of the essential oil

● Antidepressant	● Digestive
● Anti-inflammatory	● Fungicide
● Antiseptic	● Hypotensive
● Bactericide	● Nerve sedative
● Carminative	● Stimulant
● Choleretic	● Tonic

Main chemical components
● Limonene, Decanal, Ketones, Coumarins, Furo-coumarins, Terpene Alcohols, Aldehydes, and Monoterpenes.

Therapeutic applications
● Oral Thrush, Anxiety, Bronchitis, Dermatitis, Dyspepsia, Eczema, Digestive Spasms, Constipation, Stress, Flu, Palpitations, Colds, Fluid Retention, Nervous Tension.

Cosmetic applications
● Its purifying property makes it is extremely useful for oily skin, and for lackluster complexions. As an aid for eliminating liquids, it is also used in treatments for obesity.
● Out of all the citruses, it is the one most common as perfume, since it is very sweet and fruity. It is very suitable to add to a relaxing bath before going to sleep, because it has a nice calming effect.

Oregano

General description

This plant, a relative of marjoram, is a creeper that grows wild throughout Europe. Its hairy, aromatic stems with oval leaves rise almost half a meter from the ground and culminate in a crown of pink, white, or mauve flowers.

The essential oil is extracted by distillation of the flowers and ranges in color from dark yellow to grayish-brown. Its aroma, like the plant that flavors many Italian dishes, is intense, spicy, and hot, reminiscent of phenol. It is precisely this active ingredient (it is nearly 90% phenol) that renders oregano essential oil one of the most antiseptic known in aromatherapy as it.

Latin name:
Origanum vulgare
Family:
Labiatae

Main chemical components
- Thymol, Cineol, Carvacrol, Borneol, Beta-Bisabolene, Limonene, Alpha-Pinene, Beta-Pinene, Myrcene, Camphene, Alpha-Terpinene.

Did you know...?
- *The name of this plant comes from Greek and means "joy of the mountain" ("oros" is "mountain" and "ganos," "joy").*

Therapeutic properties of the essential oil

- Analgesic
- Antioxidant
- Antiparasitic
- Antiseptic
- Antispasmodic
- Carminative
- Diuretic
- Emenagogue
- Expectorant
- Fungicide
- Stomachic
- Sudorífic

Therapeutic applications
- Abscess, Eructation, Psychosomatic Disorders, Asthma, Bronchitis, Sciatica, Colic, Diarrhea, Slow Digestion, Eczema, Flatulence, Boils, Herpes, Anorexia, Back Pain, Fungal Infections, Migraine, Neuralgia, Pediculosis (lice), Insect Bites, Psoriasis, Pneumonia, Fluid Retention, Rheumatism, Premenstrual Syndrome, Cough, Tuberculosis.

Cosmetic applications
- Oregano essential oil is used in cosmetics to combat cellulite and help to reduce fluid retention.

Advisory

● *It is very important that you make sure to buy pure oregano essential oil, because often what is sold is synthetic.*

Patchouli

Latin name:
Pogostemon patchouli
Family:
Labiatae

General description

Patchouli is a shrub that is one meter tall and native to tropical Asia. It is now grown in many other places for the sole purpose of producing essential oil.

It has large, hairy, and aromatic leaves, and bluish-white flowers. To obtain the essential oil the leaves are dried and fermented, then subjected to steam distillation. The result is a somewhat viscous, amber substance with a rich, lingering, and very distinct earthy fragrance that improves as time passes, although the color can turn dark orange.

Main chemical components
● Benzoic Aldehyde, Cinnamic Aldehyde, Eugenol, Cadinene, Carvone, Caryophyllene, Caerulein, Humulene, Patchoulol, and Seychellene.

Did you know…?
● *Although this oil has been used for thousands of years in India, it didn't arrive in Europe until the late nineteenth century. It was fashionable to make oneself seem more exotic by using perfume with patchouli in it. The 1960s were hippie paradise, and everything from India became fashionable. It was the decade in which patchouli was used the most as perfume.*

Advisory
● *If applied in small doses, it has a sedative effect, whereas if the dose is higher, it can have the opposite effect and become a stimulant.*

Therapeutic applications
● Anxiety, Depression, Diarrhea, Eczema, Stress, Frigidity, Wounds, Mycosis, Athlete's Foot, Psoriasis, Fluid Retention.

Cosmetic applications
● It suppresses the appetite, so it is helpful for weight loss. In addition, being a diuretic it helps eliminate fluid retention and combats cellulite. Thus because it has regenerative, tonic, and astringent properties, it helps tighten sagging skin resulting from a rapid or pronounced weight loss.
● With regard to the skin, it is also very suitable for the complexion, for oily hair or dandruff, and for treating acne. It also has a cooling and soothing effect on dry, cracked skin.
● Finally, its antiperspirant and deodorant properties make it a great help if you suffer from excessive sweating.

Therapeutic properties of the essential oil

- Antidepressant
- Antiemetic
- Anti-inflammatory
- Antimicrobial
- Antioxidant
- Antiphlogistic
- Antiseptic

- Antiviral
- Aphrodisiac
- Astringent
- Carminative
- Cautery
- Cytophylactic
- Deodorant
- Diuretic

- Febrífuge
- Fungicide
- Insecticide
- Nervine
- Prophylactic
- Sedative
- Stomachic
- Tonic

Petitgrain

Latin name:
Citrus aurantium
Family:
Rutaceae

General description

Three types of essential oil come from the bitter orange. The peel of the fruit provides bitter orange, the flowers, neroli, and its leaves, petitgrain.

Bitter orange is an ornamental tree that came from China to Spain, brought by the Arabs in the time of the Muslim conquest. Its fruit is smaller and also more bitter than that of the sweet orange, which is suitable for consumption.

The essential oil owes its name to the fact that originally it was extracted from the fruits when they were still at an early stage and were tiny green grains. At present, the oil is removed by distillation from the leaves and young branches of the bitter orange tree. Its properties closely resemble those of neroli essential oil, of which we have spoken, and differ mainly in that they are

less sedating.

The color can range from a pale yellow to a darker amber, and the aroma is fresh, citrusy, and floral, reminiscent of neroli but less intense.

Did you know…?

● *Because it is a mild sedative, it helps to overcome dependency on sleeping pills and tranquilizers. It is a natural way to fall asleep and to regain peace of mind.*

Cosmetic applications

- Petitgrain essential oil gives very good results in the treatment of skin suffering from acne on account of its antiseptic and rubefacient properties. It is also recommended for oily skin and hair. In addition, it controls excessive sweating, and it works very well as a deodorant.
- Furthermore, petitgrain essence is one of the most widely used in perfumery as a base for cologne because of its sweet, citrus aroma, very fresh and reminiscent of lavender. It is a "classic" in perfumery.

Main chemical components

- Linalool, Linalyl Acetate, Geranyl Acetate, Limonene, and Geraniol.

Therapeutic applications

- Anxiety, Mental Confusion, Convalescence, Dyspepsia, Doubt, Stress, Mental Fatigue, Nervous Exhaustion, Flatulence, Boils, Chronic Hepatitis, Loss of Appetite, Insomnia, Fear, Nervousness, Rheumatism.

Therapeutic properties of the essential oil

Anti-infective	Digestive Nervine
Anti-inflammatory	Digestive Stimulant
Antirheumatic	Refresher
Antiseptic	Relaxant
Antispasmodic	Stimulant
Deodorant	Stomachic

Pine

Latin name:
Pinus sylvestris
Family:
Coníferae

General description

This conifer is also known as "white pine" and grows in the colder areas of Europe, Russia, and the United States. It is an evergreen tree with green needles and reddish brown bark. It has orange flowers and brown pinecones with pointy tips.

The essential oil is extracted by distillation of the needles, pinecones, and tender branches. It is very fluid and transparent, with a slight yellow hue. Its aroma is very balsamic and comforting, smells clean, and provides freshness.

Main chemical components
● Bornyl Acetate, Borneol, Terpinyl Acetate, Camphene, Limonene, Cadinol, Cadinene, Dipentene, Phellandrene, Pinene, and Sylvestrene.

Did you know…?
● *Native Americans burned pinecones in their camps to keep themselves safe from mosquitoes. Furthermore, they covered their mattresses with pine needles to repel fleas and lice and boiled the leaves to make a beverage that protected them from scurvy, owing to the high content of vitamin C in the leaves.*

Advisory
● *Always purchase essential oil of* Pinus sylvestris. *There are other types of pine that can become toxic, as in the case of Pinus pumilio (dwarf pine).*
● *Given its hypertensive properties, you should not use it if you have high blood pressure. It is not advisable to apply it on sensitive the skin of children or the elderly.*

Therapeutic applications
● Allergies, Arthritis, Rheumatoid Arthritis, Asthma, Fatigue, Low Self Esteem, Bronchitis, Bursitis, Gallstones, Convalescence, Diabetes, Eczema, Sclerosis, Scurvy, Mental Fatigue, Nervous Fatigue, Stomach Pain, Gout, Hepatitis, Poor Circulation, Pediculosis (lice), Athlete's Foot, Prostate Problems, Psoriasis, Pneumonia, Insect Repellent, Rheumatism, Chilblains, Scabies, Sinusitis, Premenstrual Stress, Tuberculosis.

Cosmetic applications
● Pine essential oil is used to make bath products such as gel, shampoo, deodorant, and refreshing cologne, but there are no known applications in cosmetic treatments.

Therapeutic properties of the essential oil

- Adrenal Stimulant
- Anthelmintic
- Anti-inflammatory
- Antimicrobial
- Antineuralgic
- Antiphlogistic
- Antirheumatic
- Antiseptic
- Antiscorbutic
- Antiviral
- Bactericide
- Balsamic
- Cholagogue
- Circulatory Stimulant
- Decongestant
- Deodorant
- Diuretic
- Fungicide
- Lymphatic Decongestant
- Nerve Stimulant
- Hypertensive
- Hypoglycemic
- Insecticide
- Restorative
- Rubefacient
- Sudorific
- Tonic

Rose

Latin name:
Rosa damascena
and *Rosa centifolia*
Family:
Rosaceae

General description

There are multiple varieties and species of roses. For thousands of years they have adorned gardens and halls, and perfumed queens and courtesans. They remainvery much a part of our daily lives. It is the queen of perfumes, and the flower par excellence.

From its thorny bush of dark green leaves bloom roses of every hue and aromatic intensity. There are roses of all sizes and varieties.

However, out of all of them, aromatherapy utilizes the essential oil of *Rosa damascene* (also known as Alexandria or Damask Rose) and *Rosa centifolia* (Rose of a Hundred Leaves, or Roman Rose). The chromatic varieties are pink or purple. They are extracted from the Damask Rose by distillation of the petals through cold enfleurage and from the Roman Rose with volatile solvents. With this last method an absolute is absolute,

but even if used for cosmetics and perfumes, it is not suitable for therapy, due to traces of solvent in the dilution.

This is often the most expensive of all oils, because its distillation requires a large quantity of raw material. It is estimated that five tons of flowers are required to make one liter of essential oil. This explains why it is usually sold in tiny (and expensive) 1 ml. vials.

Did you know...?
● *Recognition of the sensual power of rose essential oil dates back to ancient cultures and continues in the present day. It is said that when Cleopatra seduced Mark Antony, she anointed his whole body with this fragrant essence.*

Main chemical components
● Geranic Acid, Eugenol, Citronellol, Farnesol, Geraniol, Nerol, Rhodinol, Stearoptene, and Myrcene.

Cosmetic applications
● Rose essential oil is very beneficial for all skin types, especially dry, tired, or sensitive ones.
● It is present in many perfumes and in rose hydrolate, which is an exceptional tonic for all skin types.

Therapeutic properties of the essential oil

● Aphrodisiac	● Depurative
● Antidepressant	● Emenagogue
● Antispasmodic	● Hemostatic
● Antiphlogistic	● Hepatic
● Antiseptic	● Hepatic Tonic
● Antiviral	● Laxative
● Astringent	● Splenetic
● Bactericide	● Stomachich
● Choleretic	● Stomachic Tonic
● Cordial Tonic	● Uterine Tonic

Therapeutic applications
● Anorexia, Anxiety, Asthma, Headache, Jealousy, Cholecystitis, Liver Congestion, Conjunctivitis, Depression, Discouragement, Sore Throat, Infertility, Constipation, Stress, Hay Fever, Frigidity, Bleeding, Impotence, Loss of Appetite, Insomnia, Anger, Leukorrhea, Poor Circulation, Melancholy, Menopause, Menorrhagia, Irregular Menstruation, Nausea, Ophthalmia, Resentment, Premenstrual Syndrome, Nervous Tension, Coughs, Uterine Disorders, Grief, Vomiting

Rosemary

General description

Rosemary, which means "dew of the sea" in Latin, has been long known in Mediterranean cultures for its great therapeutic benefits. The Egyptians, Greeks and Romans used it, and legend has it that the flowers turned blue when the Virgin Mary draped her cloak over a rosemary plant during the flight to Egypt.

History has proven its healing abilities, and some people now call it the "Mediterranean ginseng" owing to its multiple benefits and applications.

This plant is grown throughout the world, but the essential oil is produced in Spain, France, and Morocco. All of it is aromatic, from the long stems of narrow, silvery-green leaves to the small blue or purple flowers.

Latin name:
Rosmarinus officinalis
Family:
Labiatae

The oil is extracted from the leaves and flowers by distillation. It is pale yellow with a very fluid texture. The aroma is penetrating and refreshing, with a strong herbaceous note reminiscent of mint, providing a clean and fresh feeling.

Main chemical components
● Borneol, Cuminic Aldehyde, Bornyl Acetate, Camphor, Cineol, Caryophyllene, Camphene, and Pinene.

Did you know…?
● *In England, in former days, it was customary to wear a bag of rosemary leaves around the neck in order to avoid getting colds and to feel safe from the plague. It was also placed around the right arm to raise one's spirits or under children's pillows to protect them from nightmares.*

Therapeutic applications

● Alopecia, Amenorrhea, Tonsillitis, Anemia, Apathy, Arteriosclerosis, Asthma, Bronchitis, Bursitis, Gallstones, Severe Headache, Cirrhosis, Chlorosis, Cholecystitis, colitis, Weakness, Depression, Dermatitis, Dizziness, Diarrhea, Dysmenorrhea, Dyspepsia, Eczema, Edema, Epilepsy, Muscle Spasms (cramps), Stress, Mental Fatigue, Flatulence, Gout, Flu, Injuries, Hypercholesterolemia, Hypertension, Hysteria, Vaginal Hypotonia, Jaundice, Leukorrhea, Poor Circulation, Migraine, Palpitations, Pediculosis (lice), Fluid Retention, Colds, Rheumatism, Chilblains, Scabies, Tuberculosis, Whooping Cough, Liver Disorders, Nervous Disorders, Varicose Veins.

Cosmetic applications

● Rosemary essential oil also has excellent cosmetic applications because it is astringent and antioxidant. For example, it firms skin that is sagging due to aging or excessive or rapid weight loss. In addition, it stimulates hair growth and gives very good results with oily hair or dandruff.
● Skin with acne problems improves with treatment, and dry, mature skin rehydrates and revitalizes. The famous regenerating and revitalizing Water of Hungary was made with a base of rosemary, lemon, rose, melissa, neroli, and mint. It be-

Advisory

● *We do not recommend rosemary essential oil if you are pregnant or suffer from seizures. During a leg massage, it should not be applied directly on varicose veins.*

gan to be offered commercially in the fourteenth century. The recipe for the rejuvenating lotion came from Queen Elizabeth, the de facto ruler of Hungary, who at the age of 72 fell in love with the king of Poland. You can still find it in specialty shops and enjoy its benefits.

Therapeutic properties of the essential oil

● Analgesic	● Carminative	● Hypertensive
● Antidepressant	● Cephalic	● Hypotensive
● Antispasmodic	● Cautery	● Nervine
● Antimicrobial	● Cholagogue	● Restorative
● Antioxidant	● Choleretic	● Rubefacient
● Antiparasitic	● Cordial	● Stimulant
● Antirheumatic	● Diuretic	● Stomachic
● Antiseptic	● Emenagogue	● Sudorífic
● Aphrodisiac	● Fungicide	● Vulnerary
● Astringent	● Hepatic	

Sandalwood

Latin name:
Santalum album
Family:
Santalaceae

General description

The sandalwood tree grows in eastern India and Southeast Asia. During the first seven years of its life it is semi-parasitic, rooted in nearby plants and trees, which it ends up killing when it reaches their roots. After this period, it requires about thirty years of growth before its wood can be harnessed by the industries of essential oils, perfumes, and cosmetics. It is also widely used in construction, because its wood repels termite attacks.

By distillation, the essential oil is extracted from dried ground chips of the heartwood (the heart of the trunk), because the bark and sapwood are odorless. It is for this reason, and its long period of growth, that it has been classified as a protected tree by governments, lest its exploitation lead to its extinction.

Unlike the rest of the essential oils, which have

Did you know…?
● *Sandalwood essential oil has been present for thousands of years in Hindu, Arabic, Chinese, Tibetan, and Egyptian pharmacopoeia. Its multiple recognized therapeutic effects make it practically essential in any aromatherapist's consultation.*

Advisory
● *Because it is non-toxic, non-irritating or sensitizing, it is a very gentle emollient for the skin. Also, it can be used without problems throughout pregnancy.*

an expiration date, sandalwood should be stored for half a year before its use in order to acquire all of the active ingredients and the right perfume. After this time, it turns dark yellow and acquires a viscous texture and an aroma that is very balsamic, sweet, oriental, fruity, and very persistent. It stays on clothing even after it is washed. Sandalwood has magnificent effects not only on our bodies, but also our emotional and spiritual selves are affected by its beneficial capacities. It provides peace, balance, facilitates meditation, and enhances self-esteem, in addition to alleviating concerns, fears, and negative

nia, Laryngitis, Lumbago, Meditation, Fear, Nausea, Neuralgia, Obsessions, Itching, Colds, Nervous Tension, Cough, Tuberculosis, Urethritis, Varicose Veins, Vomiting.

Cosmetic applications

- Sandalwood essential oil is one that is most used in cosmetic applications for the skin due to its emollient, antiseptic, anti-inflammatory, healing, and astringent properties. It is very useful for acne and for all skin types, especially mature skin.
- Its rich, deep aroma, with a woody note, makes it also suitable for male cosmetics. On account of this, it is usually present in the composition of aftershave lotions. It has the added benefit of relieving itching and razor burns.

emotions. Also, we should not forget its proven reputation as an aphrodisiac.

Main chemical components

- Santalol (Alpha and Beta Santalol), Furfural, and Santalene.

Therapeutic applications

- Abscesses, Anxiety, Bronchitis, Sciatica, Cystitis, Depression, Dermatitis, Diarrhea, Sore Throat, Eczema, Stress, Frigidity, Gonorrhea, Hemorrhoids, Impotence, Indigestion, Insecurity, Insom-

Tea Tree

General description

Latin name:
*Melaleuca
alternifolia*
Family:
Myrtaceae

Tea tree essential oil comes from an Australian shrub. It has leaves that end in a point and yellow or purple flowers. Its name comes from the crew of Captain Cook, whose members drank an infusion made from the leaves of this shrub when they first arrived on the continent.

The oil, incorporated into aromatherapy in the seventies, is extracted from the leaves and twigs by steam distillation. A pale yellow color, its smell is rough and earthy with a note of camphor, but it is a clean, masculine scent, warm and cool at the same time.

It is a very versatile oil. It acts on the immune system and is seemingly a "cure all," given its wide range of therapeutic and cosmetic applications.

.

Did you know...?
● *The Aborigines of Australia used the plant to treat infected wounds. Currently the oil is being studied as a possible treatment for HIV.*

Main chemical components
● Terpineol, Cineole, Cymene, Pinene, and Terpinene

Therapeutic applications
● Abscesses, Athlete's Foot, Asthma, Asthenia, Bronchitis, Candidiasis, Chilblains, Colds, Cystitis, Depression, Cardiac Fatigue, Fever, Flu, Folliculitis, Genital Infections, Gingivitis, Gum Disease, Hay Fever, Injuries, Insect Bites, Intestinal Inflammation, Intestinal Parasites, Nervousness, Ovarian Congestion, Otolaryngologic Infections, Pneumonia, Psoriasis, Radiation Injuries, Skin Burns, Sinusitis, Tuberculosis, Vaginitis, Varicose Veins, Whooping Cough.

Cosmetic applications
● Tea tree essential oil is used above all for skin care. It supports the care and treatment of oily skin. Furthermore, it softens the marks produced by the herpes virus or varicella and helps regenerate the cracked skin.
● Tea tree oil is very useful for teenagers, because it has also been shown to be highly effective in cases of acne.

Advisory
● *If you use it pure, it is always a good idea to try a drop on the skin to test for an allergic reaction. Once proved to be safe, you should apply it only to the affected area.*

Therapeutic properties of the essential oil

- Analgesic
- Antibiotic
- Antifungicide
- Anti-inflammatory
- Antiparasitic
- Antiprurític
- Antiseptic
- Antiviral
- Bactericide
- Balsamic
- Cautery
- Cordial
- Cutaneous tonic
- Expectorant
- Fungicide
- Inmunostimulant
- Insecticide
- Nerve tonic
- Sudorífic
- Vulnerary

Thyme

Latin name:
Thymus vulgaris
Family:
Labiatae

General description

The thyme plant is native to the Mediterranean basin. It is found in more than three hundred species. It grows throughout the world, in warm climates and Iceland alike. For this reason, its active ingredients can vary, and there are different chemotypes, such as linalool or thymol, depending on which chemical is predominant.

The plant is about 30 cm. high, with small stems, aromatic dark green leaves and tiny mauve flowers. The aroma of the leaves can vary from a fragrance that evokes the lemon to a note of caraway or orange.

The essential oil is distilled from the leaves and flowers. It has a viscous, greasy consistency, is colorless, and its scent is identical to that of the plant, only much more intense. If the essential oil is packed in metal containers, the content oxidizes and turns red. However, when stored in dark glass bottles, it remains transparent, making it more likely that the active ingredients remain intact.

Main chemical components
● Thymol, Carvacrol, Borneol, Linalool, Geraniol, Geranyl Acetate, Menthone, p-Cymene, Pinene, Thujanol, and Triterpenic Acid.

Did you know…?
● *Thyme has been used for its medicinal properties since the time of the Sumerians, five millennia ago. Since then it has been the main ingredient in the traditional remedies of all Mediterranean cultures and has occupied, and occupies, an important place in their mythologies, cuisines, and pharmacies.*

Advisory

● *We do not recommend thyme essential oil if you are pregnant or suffer seizures. During a leg massage, it should not be applied directly on varicose veins.*

Cosmetic applications

● The antiseptic and astringent properties of thyme essential oil recommend it for oily hair, alopecia, and skin with acne problems. Moreover, because it stimulates circulation and the immune system, it helps regulate and regenerate the skin.

● These benefits are also noticeable in people who want to lose weight, and thyme is often present in massages for combating cellulite and obesity.

Therapeutic applications

● Abscess, Eructation, Asthma, Fatigue, Gastrointestinal Atony (slow digestion), Bronchitis, Candidiasis, Cystitis, Dermatitis, Diarrhea, Dyspepsia, Muscle Aches, Eczema, Muscle Spasms (cramps), Stomatitis, Stress, Pharyngitis, Cardiac Fatigue, Flatulence, Gout, Flu, Hypertension, Loss of Appetite, Insomnia, Poor Circulation, Ear Infections, Intestinal Parasites, Childbirth, Insect Bites, Pleurisy, Prostatitis, Psoriasis, Burns, Rheumatism, Rhinitis, Sinusitis, Chronic Cough, Tuberculosis, Urethritis, Vaginitis.

Therapeutic properties of the essential oil

● Anthelmintic	● Astringent	● Fungicide
● Antibacterial	● Balsamic	● Hypertensive
● Antispasmodic	● Carminative	● Nervine
● Antimicrobial	● Cautery	● Orexigenic
● Antioxidant	● Cordial tonic	● Rubefacient
● Antirheumatic	● Cough suppressant	● Stimulant
● Anti-toxic	● Diuretic	● Sudorific
● Aphrodisiac	● Emenagogue	● Tonic
● Antiviral	● Expectorant	● Uterine tonic

Violet

General description

The scent of the violet is, after the rose, one of the most feminine that nature provides. But it is not only pleasing, it has the therapeutic ability to revitalize the heart, help to overcome emotional setbacks, and to relieve coughs. These are just some examples of the various benefits of this tiny flower whose fragrance is reputed to be an aphrodisiac.

It is a small plant about 15 cm. tall, with thin stems and simple leaves, and elongated pedunculated flowers of a deep violet color with soft and sweet perfume. It is native to the Mediterranean basin, China, and Japan, but it is now cultivated in tropical and subtropical regions worldwide. Essential oil is obtained from the leaves by distillation, and an absolute from the flowers by extraction with volatile solvents. The absolute is used in perfumery because small traces of solvents are not recommended for therapy. The aroma is floral, sweet, lingering, and relaxing.

Latin name:
Viola odorata
Family:
Violaceae

Therapeutic properties of the essential oil

- Anti-inflammatory
- Antirheumatic
- Antiseptic
- Aphrodisiac
- Circulatory stimulant
- Cough suppressant
- Decongestant
- Diuretic
- Expectorant
- Sedative

Main chemical components
- Irone, Benzyl Alcohol, Eugenol, and Monadienol.

Therapeutic applications
- Anxiety, Nervous Exhaustion, Low Self-Esteem, Bronchitis, Dermatitis, Eczema, Mental Fatigue, Skin Infections, Insomnia, Anger, Poor Circulation, Kidney Problems, Colds, Rheumatism, Stress, Sadness over Abandonment.

Cosmetic applications
- Violet has emollient properties that deeply moisturize mature skin. In addition, its decongestant and antiseptic properties give good results in treating acne and caring for oily skin.

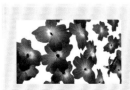

Did you know…?
- *Traditionally, violet flowers were used to prepare syrup for coughs and colds.*

Advisory
● *If you are pregnant you must wait until after the fourth month of gestation in order to use it without problems.*

White Birch

General description

The birch is a slender tree with an elongated canopy and can exceed 25 m. in height. Its leaves, small in size, are grouped in clusters hanging from its branches, and its fruit is similar to walnut.

There are several varieties of birch, but the most common are *Betula verrucosa* and *Betula pubescens*.

Birch is one of the trees most frequently found in the flora of northern, western, and central Europe, especially in those areas where soils are somewhat moist.

It also adapts perfectly to soils that are not excessively rich in nutrients. It is therefore a tree found in Scandinavian countries and is also common in large cities.

Herbal medicine takes advantage of the whole tree, but in aromatherapy, valuable essential oil is only extracted from the silvery

Latin name:
Betula alba
Family:
Betulaceas

Advisory
- Do not use if you are pregnant.
- Not to be confused with Sweet Birch (Betula lenta), which is toxic.

Therapeutic properties of the essential oil

- Analgesic
- Anti-inflammatory
- Antirheumatic
- Antiseptic
- Astringent
- Cautery
- Depurant
- Hypotensive

white bark and the leaves. It has a balsamic and pungent odor, with hints of smoke, leather and vegetable tar.

Main chemical components
- Lupanic Triterpenoids such as Betulinol, Lupeol, Lupandiol, and Betulinic Acid. Flavonoids, Allantoin, Betuloside, Tannins, and Suberin.

Therapeutic applications
Rheumatism, Gout, Eczema, Psoriasis, Cutaneous Ulcers.

Cosmetic applications
- Cellulite, obesity

White Camphor

General description

This tree, a member of the Laurel family, is very large and strong, and can exceed 30 m. in height. Its leaves are evergreen, and its trunk can be up to 12 m. in diameter. Its dark green leaves are serrated and elliptical, its small white flowers grow in bunches, and its fruits are dark red berries.

Camphor is a substance secreted by the tree, but it does not begin to produce it until it reaches fifty years of age. After removing this crystalline mass from the tree, the camphor is put through a steam distillation process to get a clear essential oil with a pungent odor reminiscent of eucalyptus. In former times, it was also used for mothballs that were placed among clothes.

It is a very powerful remedy that is effective for treating major diseases, such as heart failure, pneumonia and tuberculosis. However, it should only be used under the supervision of a specialist.

Latin name:
Cinnamomum camphora
Family:
 Lauraceae

Did you know...?
● *The Chinese say that this tree, which is indigenous to the East, can live more than a thousand years.*
Ancient camphor tree

Therapeutic properties of the essential oil

● **Analgesic**	● **Hypertensive**
● **Anthelmínic**	● **Laxative**
● **Antidepressant**	● **Rubefacient**
● **Antipruritic**	● **Sedative**
● **Antiseptic**	● **Stimulant**
● **Antispasmodic**	● **Sudorífic**
● **Carminative**	● **Vasoconstrictor**
● **Diuretic**	● **Vulnerary**

Main chemical components
● Azulene, Borneol, Cadinene, Camphene, Carvacrol, Cineole, Citronellol, Cuminyl Alcohol, Dipentene, Eugenol, Phellandrene, Pinene, Safrole, and Terpineol

Therapeutic applications
● Acne, Bronchitis, Colic, Bruising, Weakness, Depression, Diarrhea, Toothache, Shock, Constipation, Fever, Flatulence, Gout, Wounds, Hypotension, Inflammation, Insomnia, Heart Failure, Anger, Pneumonia, Intestinal Parasites, Burns, Cold, Retention Of Urine, Rheumatism, Nervous Tension, Sprains, Tuberculosis, Ulcers, Vomiting

Cosmetic applications
● It is very useful in caring for oily skin.

Winter Savory

General description

The two varieties of savory, cultivated and wild, are very similar, but in aromatherapy only the wild, mountain variety is used. This plant, which has narrow leaves and fragrant flowers, has a hairy stem and a branched, woody base.

Today, savory is a common plant found throughout the Mediterranean basin, but it likely originated on the coast of the Black Sea and the easternmost coast of the Mediterranean Sea.

Its essential oil is extracted by distillation of its leaves and sometimes its flowers. Its scent is very aromatic and slightly pungent, like thyme.

Latin name:
Satureja montana
Family:
Lamiaceae

Main chemical components
● Phenols such as thymol, carvacrol, cineole, cymene, and pinene

Advisory
● *Do not use if you are pregnant.*
● *It is a rubefacient and should not be used on sensitive skin.*
● *Not to be confused with cultivated savory, a major irritant.*

Therapeutic applications
● Abscesses, Canker Sores, Anorexia, Aids Treatment, Asthma, Scars, Cuts, Depression, Dyspepsia, Stress, Flatulence, Frigidity, Impotence, Sores, Insect Bites, Burns.

Cosmetic applications
● Very effective for treating acne and present in many hygiene products.

Did you know...?
● *The Greeks considered this plant to be aphrodisiac. Since those times, this plant has been used in cooking and in folk medicine.*

Therapeutic properties of the essential oil

● **Anti-infection**
● **Antiseptic**
● **Aphrodisiac**
● **Expectorant**
● **Stomachic**
● **Tonic**

Yarrow

Latin name:
Achillea millefolium
Family:
Asteraceae

General description

The yarrow plant has numerous therapeutic properties that have been known since ancient times. It came to be considered a sacred plant in many ancient cultures, such as the Chinese and the Greek. It is a medium-sized grass that grows in sunny areas throughout most of the northern hemisphere. It has lanceolate leaves and clusters of pinkish white flowers.

The essential oil is extracted by steam distillation from dried clusters of these flowers. It is a particular shade of blue or dark green, very liquid, and smells fresh, sweet, and herbaceous with a slight note of camphor.

Main chemical components
● Borneol, Azulene, Cineol, Limonene and Pinene.

Did you know…?
● *In ancient traditional Chinese medicine the exalted quality of perfect balance is attributed to yarrow because the plant comprises the perfect union of yin and yang.*

Therapeutic properties of the essential oil

● Antispasmodic	● Digestive
● Antiphlogistic	● Diuretic
● Anti-inflammatory	● Expectorant
● Antipyretic	● Febrifuge
● Antirheumatic	● Hemostatic
● Antiseptic	● Hypertensive
● Astringent	● Stimulant
● Carminative	● Stomachic
● Cautery	● Tonic
● Cholagogue	

Therapeutic applications
● Amenorrhea, Arteriosclerosis, Rheumatoid Arthritis, Bursitis, Scars, Cystitis, Colic, Diarrhea, Dysmenorrhea, Eczema, Bed-wetting, Muscle Spasms (cramps), Constipation, Stress, Lack of Defenses, Fibroids, Fever, Flatulence, Flu, Hemorrhoids, Wounds, Hypertension, Indigestion, Urinary Tract Infections, Insomnia, Migraine, Burns, Colds, Chilblains, Nervous Tension, Sadness, Thrombosis, Fallen Uterus, Varicose Veins.

Cosmetic applications
● Its powerful regulatory effect helps to improve the appearance and health of dry skin and problem skin with acne or scars. In addition, it is also an excellent hair tonic that promotes hair growth.

Advisory

● *You should not apply pure essential oil directly on varicose veins, chilblains or other areas affected by circulatory disorders. It should always be diluted in a vegetable oil carrier.*

● *Furthermore, it is not recommended to use during pregnancy and can cause headaches if you exceed the dosage.*

Ylang Ylang (or Cananga)

General description

Latin name:
Cananga odorata
Family:
Annonaceae

The exotic ylang ylang flower is native to tropical Asia and grows on islands such as Indonesia, the Philippines, Madagascar, and Reunion. It is a medium-sized tree with drooping, delicate branches and elongated bright leaves that hang down. At the base of the leaves grow clusters of precious flowers, which can be mauve, pink, or yellow. The essential oil is extracted from the flowers by steam distillation. The best quality is that of yellow flowers. Of a very pale amber color, it has a very fluid texture. The aroma is fresh and spicy at the same time, with a very exotic balsamic note, and a powerful, voluptuous, and sensual floral fragrance.

Main chemical components
● Benzoic Acid, Farnesol, Geraniol, Linalool, Benzyl Acetate, Eugenol, Linalyl Acetate, Linalyl Benzoate, Safrole, Cadinene, Caryophyllene, Cresol, and Pinene.

Therapeutic applications
● Anxiety, Low Self-Esteem, Recovery from Cesarean, Postpartum Depression, Stress, Frigidity, Frustration, Hypertension, Hysteria, Impotence, Intestinal Infections, Food Poisoning, Anger, Fear, Palpitations, Panic, Insect Bites, Shock, Tachycardia, Nervous Tension, Typhus.

Cosmetic applications
● An antiseborreic, it is an oil that not only helps regulate oily skin, but also dry, because it has a rebalancing effect on the sebaceous glands. It is also used to make tonics to stimulate hair growth and to prevent the scalp from becoming oily and from developing seborrheic eczema. Moreover, the oil is very beneficial for brittle nails and hair with split ends.
● Very often used in perfumery, it has aptly earned the moniker "perfume tree" on account of its rich, exotic floral fragrance, which is highly valued.

Did you know…?
In Malaysian the name "ylang ylang" signifies "flower of flowers." This essential oil is widely used in the islands of the Pacific and is applied to the hair along with cocoanut oil.

Therapeutic properties of the essential oil

- ● Aphrodisiac
- ● Antidepressant
- ● Anti-infective
- ● Antiseborrheic
- ● Antiseptic
- ● Circulatory stimulant
- ● Euphoric
- ● Hypotensive
- ● Nervine
- ● Regulator
- ● Nerve sedative
- ● Tonic
- ● Uterine tonic

Essential oils for the body

Abscesses and boils

Description

Abcesses are painful and are formed when pus accumulates in body tissue as a result of a bacterial infection. Boils are similar but are formed in a hair follicle, that is, the root of a hair.

Both usually originate as a consequence of a hormonal imbalance in people who suffer from acne or blood disorders such as diabetes. They also appear in times of stress or exhaustion and when people do not follow a balanced diet. Although

there are many essential oils that can help heal abscesses and boils, you should always see a doctor, especially if they are in the joints or a ganglion on the chest or abdomen, because this can lead to sepsis, or a widespread infection.

Aromatherapy remedies

- In the early stages of the abscess or boil, you can apply a few drops of tea tree, then spread castor oil on top of it, and heat the affected area.
- You can make a warm compress to which have been added 5 drops of cajeput, thyme and lemon, or chamomile, lavender and tea tree. Do not exceed 15 drops. Place a compress on the affected area twice daily for a quarter of an hour.
- You can also make a poultice with oatmeal to which a few drops of oregano or tea tree have been added. Put it directly on the abscess or boil and leave it there as long as necessary.
- To lance the infection, boil a cloth or towel in water to which has been added a drop of any of the previously mentioned essential oils and ap-

ply it as hot as your skin can handle.
- This remedy is also very effective against acne. Add 8 to 10 drops of lavender or tea tree to bath water to act as a general disinfectant.

Acne

Description

This is a very common disease of the sebaceous glands of the skin, which occurs mainly in adolescence, when major hormonal changes are taking place.

Although it usually appears on the face, it can also emerge on the back and chest. The treatment is the same, and good hygiene is essential. In addition, it is advisable to follow a healthy and balanced diet. Stress and lack of exercise contribute to the problem, so habits need to be changed overall.

Essential oils are very effective in treating this cutaneous problem, and it is a good practice to concentrate on one or the same mixture throughout the treatment in order to enhance its activity. For example, if you choose lavender, it should be present in the bath, the sauna, dur-

Recommended essential oils

- Basil
- Cajeput
- Chamomile
- Clary Sage
- Eucalyptus
- Geranium
- Juniper
- Lavender
- Lemon
- Myrrh
- Oregano
- Patchouli
- Palmarosa
- Rosemary
- Sandalwood
- Savory
- Tea Tree
- Thyme

ing local cleaning, massages, and compresses, etc.

Essential oils do not make the skin greasy, although it might seem so. On the contrary, those that are suitable for this problem exert a regulatory function on the sebaceous glands, so they normalize oily skin.

Aromatherapy remedies

● Make two applications with the two essential oils provided below. In the first, massage clean skin thoroughly with oil until it penetrates. Then, do the second and apply a hot cloth to facilitate absorption.
● **Normal skin**: 50 ml. of grape seed oil, 6 drops of wheat germ oil and 10 drops of the essential oil of your choice from the list provided.
● **Sensitive skin**: 25 ml. of grape seed oil, 25 ml. almond oil, 6 drops of wheat germ oil and 10 drops of the oil of your choice from the list provided.
● Prepare a facial sauna for yourself two to three times a week with a drop of lavender, chamomile, and petitgrain. If you prefer, you can choose to add to the water only 2

or 3 drops of lavender oil, for example, or of tea tree.
● Also with clean cotton you can apply a drop of geranium, roman chamomile, or tea tree directly on one spot, but not over the entire affected area.

Recommended essential oils

● Cedar	● Myrrh
● Chamomile	● Neroli
● Cypress	● Niaouli
● Eucalyptus	● Patchouli
● Geranium	● Rosewood
● Grapefruit	● Palmarosa
● Juniper	● Petitgrain
● Lavender	● Rosemary
● Lemongrass	● Sandalwood
● Lemon	● Tea Tree
● Mandarin	● Thyme
● Mint	● Vetiver

Alopecia

Description

Alopecia refers to partial or total hair loss, which mainly tends to affect men, but in some case can also occur with women.

The source can be nervous or traumatic, such as a stressful situation, but it can also be caused by illness, a reaction to certain drugs, or childbirth.

Here we refer to alopecia, and not baldness, which has a genetic origin and cannot be cured. Aromatherapy stimu-

Recommended essential oils

● Cedar	● Melissa
● Chamomile (Roman)	● Grapefruit
● Clary Sage	● Rosemary
● Lavender	● Yarrow
	● Ylang Ylang

lates hair growth in all of the cases mentioned above, except for baldness, but it can help curb some hair loss.

Aromatherapy remedies

- Using any of the recipes provided below for a scalp massage is highly recommended. It has a triple effect, because it not only aids the absorption of the essential oils, it also stimulates circulation in the scalp and oxygenates hair follicles from underneath the skin.

- For a good massage oil mixture, add 2 drops of any of the oils on the list provided to 10 ml. of grape seed oil. Gently massage it onto the scalp and leave the mixture on for an hour or an hour and a half. Then, wash your hair with your regular shampoo to rinse it out.

- Another very useful massage oil is a mixture of 45 ml. of grape seed oil, 45 ml. of wheat germ oil and 7 to 8 drops of rosemary and lavender.

- As a usual practice, it is recommended that you add a few drops of the mentioned oils to shampoo or conditioner each time you wash your hair.

Amenorrhea

Description

"Amenorrhea" is the name given to an abnormal absence of menstruation during a woman's fertile period, between puberty and menopause. There can be several reasons, such as anorexia, depression, traumatic shock, stress, or disease.

You should not be concerned about amenorrhea if menstruation stops for three or four months. It may just be that your body has decided to take a break. However, it is good to try to restore your normal rhythms and your emotional state. Moreover, it is desirable to have a regular menstrual cycle in order to get pregnant without difficulty, if that is your wish.

The keys to recovery are a balanced diet, fresh air, exercise, and a reduction of emotional stress.

Aromatherapy remedies

- Have a massage with this oil: 20 ml. of grape seed oil, 2 drops of wheat germ oil, 4 of clary sage, and 4 of chamomile. These essential oils can al-so be substituted with 8 drops of cypress or melissa. All of these stimulate and regulate.

- You can also take a bath in very hot water (not to exceed 15 minutes) to

Recommended essential oils

- Angelica
- Carrot
- Celery
- Ceylon Cinnamon
- Chamomile
- Clary Sage
- Cypress
- Fennel
- Hyssop
- Melissa
- Myrrh
- Rose

which has been added a few drops of any of the recommended oils.

Amigdalitis

Description

Inflammation of the throat may have its origin in a bacterial or viral infection. When the lymphatic glands situated at the back of the throat become inflamed on either side, it indicates the tonsils.

There can be many causes, from a lowering of defenses by stress to a poor diet or a bad cold.

Tonsillitis is often accompanied by a high fever, sore throat, inflammation of the back of the mouth, and painful swallowing. Other symptoms may include dizziness, headache, and general inflammation of all the nodes of the body.

Aromatherapy remedies

- What is fundamental for a sore throat, the popular name given to this condition, is to prevent its occurrence by increasing defenses. To prevent infections in the winter, you can gargle in the morning and evening with a glass of water to which have been added a drop of tea tree, cajuput, geranium, lavender, niaouli, pepper, rose, or rosemary.
- If you have a sore throat, you can add 2 drops of any others on the recommended list to the gargling solution and repeat five or six times a day.
- You can also make massage oil with 50 ml. of sweet almond oil and 8 drops of tea tree, lavender, or lemon. Gently massage the area of the throat in the morning and in the evening.

Recommended essential oils

- Cajeput
- Cedar
- Celery
- Ceylon Cinnamon
- Clary Sage
- Eucalyptus
- Frankincense
- Geranium
- Ginger
- Hyssop
- Lavender
- Lemon
- Marjoram
- Mint
- Myrrh
- Niaouli
- Pine
- Pepper
- Sandalwood
- Rosemary
- Rose
- Tea Tree

Anemia

Description

Many people suffer from anemia on occasion, since it is the most common blood disease.

It consists of having low levels of hemoglobin, which is the substance that provides oxygen to the tissues. The usual symptoms are lack of appetite, pallor, fatigue, dizziness, general pain, brittle fingernails, and weakness.

The most common form of anemia is lack of iron (chlorosis), which is one of the basic components of hemoglobin. Diet plays a very important role in the recovery and should be one that is rich in B vitamins, especially B12 and folic acid. Orange juice, carrots, cabbage, ginseng, and apples are healthy foods that will help you get more vitamins and the iron you need.

Aromatherapy remedies

- A massage with this oil revitalizes your body: 50 ml. of grape seed, 2 drops of wheat germ oil, 3 of melissa, and 3 of lavender. Apply it once a day, and you will start to regain energy.
- Another remedy that gives very good results is to rub lavender or melissa essential oil directly onto the soles of the feet and the back of the hands. You can choose one oil or

Recommended essential oils

- Angelica
- Black Pepper
- Carrot
- Chamomile (German)
- Lavender
- Lime
- Melissa
- Myrrh
- Rosemary

the other, or alternate. This remedy also gives very good results in cases of anorexia nervosa.

Arthritis

Description

Inflammation of the joints is called "arthritis," and there are many types. Rheumatoid arthritis is an inflammation of the tissue around the joints. It is chronic and causes pain, swelling, and stiffness.

Arthritis can also bring fatigue, fever, anemia, and weight loss. The cause is unknown, and it affects women more often than men.

Osteoarthritis is a progressive wearing of the joint cartilage caused by age or repetitive motion. It results in decreased mobility due to the intense pain caused by friction. The connective tissue becomes inflamed and produces fluid that, in turn, causes swelling.

Aromatherapy can help people with arthritis because it relaxes the muscles and relieves pain, but it cannot repair cartilage. If this is the case, aromatherapy offers a palliative rather than curative treatment, helping to create a better quality of life.

Aromatherapy remedies

● Baths help to relax the muscles and alleviate pain. Add 1 drop of cypress, another of juniper and another of pine to hot water. If you are in a lot of pain, you can add 2 drops of cajuput or Roman chamomile.
● Another good remedy is hot compresses on the painful areas. Add to

Recommended essential oils

● Black Pepper	● Eucalyptus
● Cajeput	● Juniper
● Carrot	● Lavender
● Chamomile (Roman)	● Marjoram
	● Pine
● Cypress	● Rosemary

15 ml. of carrot carrier oil, 2 drops of pine, 2 of cypress, and 1 of lavender. Soak it up with a very hot wet towel and apply it the morning and at night.
● To relieve inflammation and pain you can also use cold compresses to which have been added a few drops of lavender, Roman chamomile or yarrow.

● If you need to reduce stiffness, apply hot compresses with 2 drops of rosemary, marjoram, or black pepper.
● A good massage oil can be made from 60 ml. of sweet almond oil and 1 drop of rosemary, eucalyptus, Roman chamomile, and lavender. It is a soothing and anti-inflammatory mixture that can be applied regularly as a preventive measure for areas that tend to be more painful.

Asthma

Description

"Asthma" is defined as muscle spasms that occur in the alveoli, located in the lungs; these narrow the bronchi due to inflammation and mucus. The main symptoms are choking, wheezing, and coughing.

The origin of this disease, which tends to be chronic, is an allergy in the majority of cases, although tobacco can also cause it. It is crucial to know the allergen that causes the inflammation and spasms, but it is not always possible to identify it. In any event, avoid pets and contact with pollen, and keep the house mite free as much as possible.

People of nervous temperament are more predisposed to asthma attacks. In fact, there is something called "stress-induced asthma," which is an attack caused by a traumatic shock or an upset. There is also asthma that is induced by exerting force, which occurs when playing sports or exercising excessively.

Aromatherapy is not the best option for treating asthma. What is certain is that inhalations with essential oils can aggravate an asthma attack, so it is absolutely not recommended. In addition, the purity of the oil cannot be guaranteed, so that the problems that could arise outnumber the advantages.

For treatment use essential oils in moderation, but only in essence diffusors, in massage oils, or a few drops on a handkerchief. To avoid aggravating the spasms, you should never use it with hot steam, so we do not recommend inhalations or hot baths.

Aromatherapy remedies

● Mix 3 to 4 drops of lavender, clary sage, or frankincense with 25 ml. of

Recommended essential oils

● Angelica	● Lime
● Basil	● Lemon
● Bergamot	● Marjoram
● Cajeput	● Melissa
● Cedar	● Mint
● Cypress	● Niaouli
● Eucalyptus	● Rosewood
● Geranium	● Sandalwood
● Fennel	● Thyme
● Frankincense	
● Jasmine	

sweet almond essential oil. Massage the back in gentle sweeping motions from the base of the neck, along the spine, and lower the hands to the sides.

● Mix 3 drops of cedar, 1 of cajuput, and 2 of mint in 15 ml. of carrier oil, and massage the chest, throat, and upper back. The motions should be upwards in order to help to clear the mucous.

● Pour a few drops of cajuput, cedar, or eucalyptus, and take three gentle but deep breaths. In the event of a severe attack, put a drop of cajuput in the palm of your hand, rub it, and cover your mouth and nose with it while inhaling deeply. Cajuput is an antispasmodic and will help you to regain a normal rhythm of breathing.

Athlete's foot

Description

This condition is caused by the fungus *Tinea pedis*, and the most common symptoms are itching between the toes and flaking of the skin on the entire affected area. When it affects the nails, they become brittle and turn an ugly whitish color. The fungus is very contagious; it can be caught in humid places, such as gymnasiums or pools where people walk barefoot.

Recommended essential oils

● Clary Sage	● Mint
● Eucalyptus	● Myrrh
● Geranium	● Patchouli
● Lavender	● Tea Tree
● Lemongrass	

Aromatherapy remedies

● Prevention is essential. Walk in shower slippers in areas prone to infection and before and after going to the gym or pool, scrub the feet with geranium or tea tree essential oil.

● If you are already infected, take footbaths in salt water with 5 drops of tea tree or clary sage for twenty minutes. Then dry them thoroughly and apply an oil prepared with 10 ml. of sweet almond oil, 2 drops of wheat germ oil, 2 of geranium and 2 more of tea tree.

● If the skin is very flaky add to 25 ml. of oil infused with calendula, 4 drops of tea tree, 4 of lavender, and 4 of myrrh.

Backache

Description

Back pain can have many causes, some deriving from the habits and practices of modern life. Leaving aside sciatica and lumbago, which due to their importance we cover separately, there exist many causes, which, although they have nothing to do with physical lesions, can result in terrible back pain.

We refer, for example, to lifting weights, walking in high heels, maintaining improper posture, playing sports without warming up the muscles, or the tensions that arise from stressful situations that can cause muscles to contract. In these cases, massage and hot baths with essential oils are two nice ways to regain wellbeing. Also, you can put a few drops of any soothing essential oil on your pillow or in a diffusor to help you fall asleep and rest throughout the night.

Aromatherapy remedies

● Muscle pain of the back responds very well to massage. Prepare 50 ml. of grape seed oil with 5 drops of lavender, marjoram, and rosemary. The effects are more potent if the massage is given after a shower or a hot bath.

● Prevention is a great ally. Therefore, before participating in any sport, you can have a massage with 50 ml. of sweet almond oil, to which have been added 10 drops of rosemary, 10 of pine, and 5 of black pepper. This warm up will help you avoid over exertion and pulled muscles.

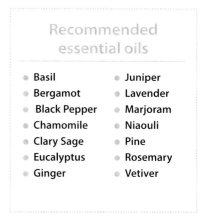

Recommended essential oils

● Basil
● Bergamot
● Black Pepper
● Chamomile
● Clary Sage
● Eucalyptus
● Ginger

● Juniper
● Lavender
● Marjoram
● Niaouli
● Pine
● Rosemary
● Vetiver

● A hot bath will quickly restore you to wellbeing and bring relief to aching muscles. Add to the bath water 8 to 10 drops of any of the recommended essential oils.

Bronchitis

Description

This disease causes inflammation of the bronchi and can be acute or chronic. In the former case it results from an infection caused by poorly healed viral or bacterial infection. For example, a cold that has not been fully cured can lead to acute bronchitis.

In the second case, the reason is the irritation of the bronchi, and there can be many causes, such as smoking, pollution or allergens.

Recommended essential oils

• Bergamot	• Marjoram
• Cajeput	• Mint
• Cedar	• Oregano
• Clary Sage	• Pine
• Eucalyptus	• Rosemary
• Frankincense	• Sandalwood
• Hyssop	• Tea Tree
• Lavender	• Thyme

In both cases, the symptoms are cough, fever, chest pain, and coughing up phlegm. Unless it is completely cured, it can result in pneumonia, which can be fatal for children and the elderly.

It is also important to correct bad postural habits and to be careful with climate changes and nervous tension, since they tend to have a major impact on the origin and development of this pulmonary condition. Another important factor to consider is exercise, which is very beneficial for prevention.

Aromatherapy remedies

● Chronic bronchitis improves with inhalations of essential oil from sage, mint, and lavender.

●To reduce mucus and relieve congestion you can have a massage on the back, chest, and throat with a blend of essential oils that have expectorant properties. For example, 4 or 5 drops of mint, lavender, and clary sage in 25 ml. of sweet almond oil or, if you prefer, angelica, hyssop, and thyme.

● If the cough is dry, use steam to relieve the irritation. Add 6 drops of sandalwood and/or frankincense to a bowl of very hot water, and inhale for five or ten minutes. If there is an infection, put in 6 drops of tree tea, hyssop, thyme and/or eucalyptus. Repeat twice a day.

● To fight the infection, put a few drops of tree tea, eucalyptus, or thyme into a diffusor. If you use cedar or marjoram at night, it will help you breathe better and not cough. If you prefer, you can put a few drops on a handkerchief, keep it to hand, and inhale several times during the day.

● Hot baths are highly recommended to recover from bronchitis. You can add 8 to 10 drops of any of the recommended essential oils. If you have a fever, however, the bath water should be cold.

Bursitis

Description

This is a very common rheumatic illness. It occurs in the joints, where the small pouch of synovial fluid located between both bones becomes inflamed and painful. The cause can be an infection, an accident, or excess repetitive movement. Tennis elbow is a classic example of this malady. Essential oils help to reduce the pain and inflammation, although they cannot cure the infection.

Aromatherapy remedies

● Mix 10 ml. of sweet almond oil, 10 drops of wheat germ oil, and 5 drops of cajuput, eucalyptus, geranium or rosemary. Gently rub the lotion on the affected area twice daily. You can also use marjoram, clove, or pine.

● If the joint is very swollen, apply cold compresses to which have been added a few drops of lavender or chamomile, which have great anti-inflammatory properties.

Recommended essential oils

- Cajeput
- Chamomile
- Clove
- Eucalyptus
- Geranium
- Marjoram
- Pine
- Yarrow

Chilblains

Description

Chilblains were very well known in former times when home heating was rudimentary, and the winter cold wreaked havoc on the health of many people.

However, today people still continue to suffer from this circulatory disorder. Bluish-red blemishes appear on parts of the body that are exposed to cold, such as the hands, the back of the legs, or the feet.

Aromatherapy remedies

● If you have very cold feet when you get home, rub them with a mixture with a base of 10 ml. of grape seed oil and 5 drops of tea tree. You can also apply a drop of pure essential oil to the chilblains and rub very gently to avoid further irritating the area.
● It is also recommended that you bathe the affected area with hot water or apply a compress with hot water and 5 drops of any of the recommended essential oils.
● To stimulate circulation, massage with a mixture of 50 ml. of sweet almond oil, 5 drops of wheat germ oil, 10 drops of rosemary, 10 of pine, 5 of black pepper, and 5 of ginger.

Recommended essential oils

- Black Pepper
- Chamomile
- Eucalyptus
- Geranium
- Ginger
- Lavender
- Lime
- Pine
- Rosemary
- Tea Tree
- Yarrow

Colds

Description

This viral infection is highly contagious and every human being has had it not once, but several times. There is a full array of airborne viruses that cause and propagate it. The symptoms, known to all, include sneezing, runny nose, sore throat, fever, malaise, itchy, watery eyes…

A bad cold can easily lead to bronchitis or sinusitis, so it is important to devote the requisite care and attention to it. There is no known cure, and treatments are always palliative. Aromatherapy is very effective in both preventing colds, and preventing them from spreading, as well as relieving symptoms and ensuring a successful recovery.

Remember that eucalyptus can be dangerous for people with asthma, because it can cause bronchial spasms. Therefore, if this pertains to you, avoid it in any of the remedies that you apply. At most, a drop on a tissue, so you can smell it, may help decongest the lungs and nasal passages.

Recommended essential oils

- Angelica
- Basil
- Bergamot
- Black Pepper
- Cajeput
- Cedar
- Ceylon Cinnamon
- Clary Sage
- Clove
- Eucalyptus
- Frankincense
- Geranium
- Hyssop
- Ginger
- Lavender
- Lemon
- Marjoram
- Melissa
- Mint
- Myrrh
- Niaouli
- Rosewood
- Pine
- Sandalwood
- Tea Tree
- Thyme
- Yarrow

In any event, there are many other options that will help you without posing any additional risks, so it would be better to decide from the list of recommended essential oils.

Aromatherapy remedies

- Since colds are very contagious, you should you clean the air in your home or your workplace of viruses. In an essence diffusor put a few drops of cinnamon, eucalyptus, thyme, niaouli, cloves, or pine. In your workplace mix essential oils with some carrier oil and soak a piece of cotton in it. Then place it on top of the radiator. This will cause the volatile components of the essential oils to evaporate and, with this, release their antiseptic properties.
- Another preventive measure is to mix 50 ml. of sweet almond oil with 1 drop of each of these essential oils: pine, niaouli, clove, and eucalyptus. Rub it on the chest, and put a little bit in your nostrils. This remedy also works well during the initial stages of a cold.
- If you feel congested, make inhalations, take a bath, or prepare a handkerchief with a few drops of the following essential oils: clove, eucalyptus, cajuput, pine and niaouli.
- If you have a cough, mix 25 ml. of sweet almond oil with 4 or 5 drops of ginger, thyme, lavender, and hyssop. Apply it to the chest and upper back a couple of times a day.
- Take a hot bath every day with 10 drops of tea tree, rosemary or thyme to combat congestion and infection. Lavender, marjoram, and bergamot can help if your body is sore and also to help you have a restorative sleep.
- In order to recover your sense of smell, you can make inhalations with hot water and a few drops of geranium, mint, or basil. This can also be added to bath water.
- If you have a sore or irritated throat, you can gargle with a little bit of hot water to which have been added 2 drops of tea tree, and 1 of lemon, geranium, or thyme.

Constipation

Description

Constipation is not a disease itself, but it indicates a physical or emotional problem that directly affects transit through the intestine. Difficulty and/or irregular bowel movements may cause, at the same time, a number of unpleasant symptoms, such as headache, stomach pain, nervous tension, headaches, fatigue, and painful bowel movements.

The onset of menstruation, stress, pregnancy, or the side effects of some drugs are some of the causes of constipation. However, the most common cause is usually a low-fiber diet and drinking very little water. Both of these factors contribute to causing

the stool to be compacted and not able to move well with the momentum of peristaltic movements. Suffering from chronic constipation may result in hemorrhoids, cellulitis, general malaise, and oily skin.

A diet rich in fiber and two liters of water a day are a great help in combating these intestinal problems. In addition, essential oils can also be an aid with this annoying health problem.

Aromatherapy remedies

● Mix 3 drops of rosemary, 3 of mint, and 3 of black pepper or ginger with 25 ml. of sweet almond oil. Twice a day massage the abdomen in a gentle circular motion in a clockwise direction.
● Take a hot bath to which has been added 8 to 10 drops of any of the recommended essential oils.
● Apply a lukewarm compress to the belly that has been soaked in hot water with some drops of any of the essential oils for relieving discomfort. To maintain the heat, place a hot water bottle on top of the compress.

Recommended essential oils

● Angelica	● Juniper
● Bergamot	● Lemon
● Black Pepper	● Lime
● Cardamom	● Mandarin
● Carrot	● Mint
● Celery	● Neroli
● Citronella	● Orange
● Coriander	● Palmarosa
● Fennel	● Petitgrain
● Geranium	● Rosemary
● Ginger	

● If you are stressed, it would help to eliminate toxins and purify the body with a total body massage with a base of depurative and digestive essential oils. We recommend that you add 50 ml. of grape seed oil, 5 of rosemary, 5 of neroli or petitgrain, and 5 of fennel or geranium.

Cramps

Description
There are several types of cramps or spasms that can occur. The cause varies, and can be, for example, excessive exercise, menstruation, premenstrual syndrome, poor circulation, or even a vitamin deficiency.

Aromatherapy can help because it relaxes muscle tension and, in turn, relieves pain. Moreover, since in many cases the cramps occur at night, essential oils can also offer the advantage of helping you to fall asleep again in a correct way.

Aromatherapy remedies

● To relax cramps, massage the area with a concentrated mixture containing 25 ml. of hazelnut oil and 5 drops of marjoram, rosemary, and lavender, plus 3 drops of black pepper or ginger.
● To prevent cramps after exercise, mix 50 ml. of grape seed oil with 8 or 10 drops of rosemary, marjoram, and lavender. Then, take a hot shower and liberally massage the entire body, lingering on the muscles that have been most worked during the exercise.
● If the cramps are from menstruation or a stomach ache, apply a warm compress to which has been added a few drops of marjoram or

clary sage. Put a hot water bottle on top to maintain the high temperature for half an hour.

● A nice hot bath with 8 or 10 drops of any of the recommended oils can help you after an intense exercise session.

Recommended essential oils

- Basil
- Mandarin
- Clary Sage
- Marjoram
- Cypress
- Niaouli
- Eucalyptus
- Pine
- Ginger
- Rosemary
- Grapefruit
- Vetiver
- Lemon

Cystitis

Description

Cystitis is a bacterial infection of the bladder that is caused by the entry of bacteria into the urethra. The symptoms of this annoying condition are continuous urination, itching and burning, desire to urinate, and even fever. If there is blood in the urine you should go to the doctor.

It occurs more often in women than in men, the urinary tract being much shorter and therefore easier to access, in addition to being much closer to the urinary meatus in the perianal area. In addition, birth control pills predispose one to contract it because they alter the intestinal flora.

Other causes of cystitis are constipation, a poorly cured cold, pregnancy, bronchitis or, even, the smell of fresh paint.

There is the medical condition called "honeymoon cystitis," which is caused by very frequent intercourse, resulting in an abnormal overgrowth of bacteria in the urethra or swelling.

Aromatherapy remedies

● Seated baths are very beneficial. Add 4 or 5 drops of the essential oil you prefer from the recommended list and remain for 20 minutes. Cold water is better because heat can further irritate the bladder. These baths are very suitable as prevention after intercourse, although they may be limited to a brief wash.

Recommended essential oils

- Angelica
- Juniper
- Bergamot
- Lavender
- Cajeput
- Niaouli
- Celery
- Palmarosa
- Cedar
- Sandalwood
- Chamomile
- Tea Tree
- Eucalyptus
- Yarrow
- Frankincense

● You can have a massage with 25 ml. of sweet almond oil and 3 drops of tea tree, sandalwood, and bergamot or lavender. Apply it to the lower abdomen or back a couple of times a day.

● You can dip cotton in 100 ml. of cold, boiled water to which have been added 10 or 12 drops of antiseptic tea tree and wash well the vulva and urethral opening.

● Rub the soles of the feet and the backs of the hands, the belly and the lower back with 25 ml. of grape seed oil and 5 drops of cajuput, juniper, niaouli, pine, or sandalwood.

Dermatitis and eczema

Description

The origin of dermatitis and eczema tends to be allergic, although it can also be caused by stress, running water, food, and air pollution.

These are two very similar skin conditions with common symptoms, such as inflammation of the skin and the formation of rashes that swell, itch, and hurt, and can result in blisters and oozing scabs. The skin is eroded and loses its natural texture, so it becomes rough, thick, and scaly. In addition, these conditions tend to leave spots.

Dermatitis may be caused by stress, whereas eczema is a skin condition caused by contact with an irritant, such as tap water, the chemical agents in the cosmetics, and metals or pollution. Stress and anxiety make it worse.

There is the so-called "diaper rash" that babies have. This is produced by the contact of urine with skin and the lack of ventilation in the diaper.

Some essential oils can cause an allergic reaction, and they are not recommended. This is why it is advisable to make a test on a small area of healthy skin before applying them to the dermatitis or eczema.

Recommended essential oils

- Angelica
- Black Pepper
- Bergamot
- Carrot
- Cedar
- Chamomile
- Cypress
- Geranium
- Frankincense
- Lavender
- Myrrh
- Patchouli
- Pine

Aromatherapy remedies

- Make a lotion with 15 ml. of sweet almond oil, 5 drops of wheat germ oil, 2 of chamomile, and 1 of carrot. Other essential oils can be used, such as lavender, cedar, or niaouli, but this should not exceed 3 drops all together.
- Another very beneficial lotion for combating eczema and dermatitis consists of the same oil carriers, but with 3 drops of myrrh or lavender. It is very suitable for reducing inflammation.
- Mix 20 ml. of grape seed oil with 4 drops of black pepper. Applying it will activate healing.
- To combat dermatitis of the face and neck make a lotion with 5 ml. of sweet almond oil, 3 drops of wheat germ oil and 1 of frankincense.

Diarrhea

Description

This digestive disorder is manifested by feces of a liquid texture and very frequent, causing abdominal pain and irritation of the bowels. It can also be accompanied by nausea, vomiting, and fever.

The causes can vary from physical to emotional. Stress, anxiety, medications, spoiled food, food intolerances, bacteria, influenza, viruses...

It is necessary to understand the cause and follow a very gentle diet, in addition to replenishing lost water-based fluids, and other specific preparations for preventing dehydration.

Aromatherapy remedies

- If caused by stress, a good remedy is to take a warm bath to which has been added 3 drops of geranium, lavender, and ginger. In this way you will regain tranquility.
- If the problem is fever and nausea, submerge yourself in a cold bath with 3 drops of mint, 3 of tea tree or thyme, and 3 of ginger.
- It is also beneficial to massage the abdomen in a circular motion in a clockwise direction with 25 ml. of grape seed oil and 4 drops of lavender, juniper, and geranium. If you believe that it has to do with a bacterial infection or a virus, add 2 drops of tea tree or thyme to the mixture.

Recommended essential oils

• Chamomile	• Lemon
• Clove	• Mint
• Cypress	• Oregano
• Geranium	• Sandalwood
• Ginger	• Tea Tree
• Juniper	• Thyme
• Lavender	

- Apply heat to the abdomen with a hot compress soaked in water and drops of any of the previously mentioned essential oils.
- A soothing and astringent massage oil can be composed of 15 ml. of sweet almond oil, 3 drops of tea tree or mint and 2 of sandalwood or geranium.

Dysmenorrhea

Description

This name is given to pain, cramps, nausea, and vomiting that occur in the first days of menstruation, caused by a hormonal imbalance that occurs in many young women during the process.

If dysmenorrhoea appears in adulthood the cause is quite different; it could be a type of pelvic inflammatory disease, an inflammation of the pelvis, or a fibroma.

It is essential to visit a gynecologist to determine the cause if dysmenorrhea appears suddenly after years of normal menstruation with little discomfort.

Aromatherapy remedies

- Take a hot bath to which has been added a few drops of cypress, chamomile, or marigold. And remember that by deeply relaxing you can also ease the symptoms.
- Apply hot compresses to which have been added a few drops of any of the previously mentioned essential oils.
- You can massage the belly and the lower back with 25 ml. of sweet almond oil, 15 ml. of evening primrose, and 4 or 5 drops of clary sage, marjoram, and lavender.

Recommended essential oils

• Caraway	• Marigold
• Cardamom	• Marjoram
• Carrot	• Melissa
• Chamomile	• Mint
• Cypress	• Neroli
• Frankincense	• Rosemary
• Geranium	• Rose
• Ginger	• Yarrow
• Lavender	

Dyspepsia

Description

Dyspepsia is a chronic disorder that is characterized by problems with digestion, which becomes slow and heavy. Heartburn, flatulence, colic, and abdominal pain are among the symptoms. It often comes from nervous eating out of anxiety or stress.

Eating too much or too quickly are two ways to cause dyspepsia, in addition to spoiled food or food intolerances.

Aromatherapy remedies

● If one of the main symptoms of your dyspepsia is that you feel nausea, put a few drops of mint in a handkerchief or a diffusor.
● If, on the other hand, indigestion is from nervous tension, take a hot bath to which have been added 8 to 10 drops in total of lavender, chamomile and clary sage.

Recommended essential oils

● Angelica	● Laurel
● Basil	● Lavender
● Black Pepper	● Lemongrass
● Caraway	● Lemon
● Cardamom	● Marjoram
● Carrot	● Melissa
● Chamomile	● Mint
● Clary Sage	● Neroli
● Fennel	● Palmarosa
● Ginger	● Petitgrain
● Juniper	● Rose

● You can also place a hot towel soaked in hot water on the belly with a few drops of lavender or chamomile. Put a hot water bottle on top of it to retain the heat until the pain has calmed down.
● A good massage oil for these cases is comprised of 25 ml. of sweet almond oil, 3 drops of lavender, 3 of chamomile, and 3 of mint. If dyspepsia is accompanied by flatulence, 2 drops of fennel may also be added.
● Another massage oil that gives good results contains 15 ml. of grape seed oil, 3 drops of mint, 1 of juniper, and 2 of caraway.

Earache

Description

An earache can be as annoying as a toothache, and as intense.

This pain can be caused by an infection in the ear, or otitis, a decayed tooth, an infection that extends from the nose to the throat, flu or sinusitis, and even the beginning of mumps.

Aromatherapy remedies

● If the pain is caused by a sore throat, gargle with a glass of warm water to which have been added 2 drops of tea tree essential oil.

Recommended essential oils

● Chamomile	● Marjoram
● Clove	● Tea Tree
● Lavender	

● Mix 5 ml. of grape seed oil with 1 drop of clove essential oil. Massage the neck and around the ear.

• Moisten a cotton ball with olive or sweet almond oil and 3 drops of lavender or chamomile and place it on the external part of the ear. This remedy can only be applied if your doctor has confirmed that you have not suffered a perforated eardrum.

Edema

Description

"Edema" is understood to be an abnormal retention of liquids produced in a part of the body. A typical example of edema is the liquid retention that some women often suffer during premenstrual syndrome or pregnancy.

However, it can also be caused by allergies, hypertension, kidney disease, heart problems, spending too much time standing, or sitting for too many hours. In these last two cases, the edema is localized in the legs or in the hands. It can also manifest around the eyes, forming bags.

We recommend that you abstain from aromatherapy during pregnancy because many essential oils have emmenagogic properties, which is to say that they regulate the menstrual cycle and can cause a miscarriage.

Aromatherapy remedies

• Take a tepid bath to which have been added 8 to 10 drops of any of the recommended essential oils.
• Prepare a massage oil with 25 ml. of sweet almond oil, 3 drops of rosemary, 3 of geranium, and 3 of fennel. Massage the specific area, and try to get a therapist to perform a lymphatic massage, which gives extraordinary results for fluid retention and is very relaxing.
• It is also advisable to vigorously rub the soles of the feet with a mixture of 15 ml. of grape seed oil and 2 or 3 drops of cypress or rosemary.
• It is also very beneficial to gently rub the solar plexus, belly, back of the hands, and soles of the feet in the morning and evening with a mixture containing 50 ml. of sweet almond oil, 5 drops of wheat germ oil, and 8 to 10 drops of any of the following essential oils: basil, cedar, cypress, or lavender.

Recommended essential oils

• Angelica	• Juniper
• Basil	• Lavender
• Carrot	• Mandarin
• Celery	• Orange
• Cedar	• Neroli
• Chamomile	• Petitgrain
• Clary Sage	• Rosemary
• Fennel	• Thyme
• Geranium	

• For swollen legs, we recommend a massage with upward strokes with 50 ml. of sweet almond oil, 5 drops of wheat germ oil, 6 drops of cypress, and 6 drops of lemon.

Fatigue

Description

Fatigue is manifested in our lives on many occasions and comes from very different circumstances. Fatigue can be caused by excessive exercise or work, but also by a tense situation, a disappointment, or a sleepless night. It can also be caused by pregnancy or a hormonal change. For example, adolescence and menopause are two phases during which a

person may feel fatigued for no apparent reason.

It not only manifests in the familiar feeling of exhaustion, but can also cause headaches or an inability to stay alert. If fatigue continues for days, you should see a doctor.

Aromatherapy remedies

● Sedative essential oils can help when you are overwhelmed by fatigue. Basil, lavender, neroli, or petitgrain are the most effective. Add 3 or 4 drops of one of them to 10 ml. of sweet almond oil and 2 drops of wheat germ oil and massage the chest, neck and temples.

● A hot bath works wonders. Any of the previously mentioned essential oils can convert a simple bath into a complete moment of wellbeing. Add 10 drops or a combination of various ones.

● Hormonal changes respond very well to cypress, geranium, chamomile, and clary sage. Add 10 drops of various ones, or only one, into a hot bath or essence diffusor and you will feel renewed.

Recommended essential oils

● Angelica	● Lavender
● Basil	● Lemongrass
● Bergamot	● Lime
● Chamomile	● Lemon
● Clary Sage	● Myrrh
● Cypress	● Orange
● Eucalyptus	● Neroli
● Fennel	● Patchouli
● Frankincense	● Petitgrain
● Geranium	● Pine
● Ginger	● Rosewood
● Grapefruit	● Tea Tree
● Jasmine	● Ylang Ylang
● Juniper	

● If the fatigue is nervous or mental, it is better to opt for a group of citrus to lift you up. Prepare a good oil massage with 10 ml. of sweet almond oil, 2 drops of wheat germ oil and 6 drops in total of one or a combination of the various oils referred to.

Fever

Description

Fever is not an illness, but a warning signal to the body that indicates the development of a viral or bacterial infection. In addition, it can also be produced by physical or mental exertion, a stressful situation, or a reaction of the body to very abrupt climate changes. The symptoms are a body temperature above 37 degrees Celsius, and alternating sensations of heat and cold and chills. Besides aromatherapy and a diet of liquids and soft foods rich in vitamin C and other natural remedies, it is very important to rest. Rest is key to recuperation, and it is advisable to stay in bed when you have a fever. If the fever lasts for more than two days, it is imperative that you consult a primary care physician in order to rule out serious diseases.

Aromatherapy remedies

● It is very useful to place a few drops of rosemary or eucalyptus in a diffusor during convalescence.

● Prepare an oil massage with 25 ml. of sweet almond oil and 5 drops of tea tree, eucalyptus, lavender, lemongrass, cajuput, rosemary, coriander, chamomile, cypress, niaouli, thyme, clove, or lemon. Massage the neck, chest, and soles of the feet a couple of times a day.

Recommended essential oilss

• Basil	• Eucalyptus
• Bergamot	• Lavender
• Cajeput	• Lemongrass
• Camphor	• Mint
• Chamomile	• Niaouli
• Citronella	• Rosemary
• Cypress	• Tea Tree
• Clove	• Thyme
• Coriander	• Yarrow

• Lukewarm baths can also lower your temperature. Add to the water up to 10 drops of one or more of these essential oils: basil, tea tree, eucalyptus, or mint. If you are too weak to take a bath, ask for a bath with a sponge soaked in water with a few drops of one or two of the aforementioned oils.

Flatulence

Description

This is a very annoying, and sometimes painful, ailment caused by the distension of the stomach or intestine as a result, usually, of fermented food in the digestive tract.

Laughter, anxiety, or shortness of breath can increase the amount of oxygen and nitrogen that enters our stomach. On the other hand, there are certain foods that when digested ferment and produce gas, such as the lactose in milk or wheat germ. Legumes and some vegetables contain sugars that also release gas during the digestive process and painfully swell the belly.

Aromatherapy remedies

• Mix 15 ml. of sweet almond oil, 4 drops of mint, 2 of juniper, and 2 of caraway. Massage the stomach or belly in circles in a clockwise direction.

Recommended essential oils

• Basil	• Laurel
• Caraway	• Lemongrass
• Cardamom	• Marjoram
• Clove	• Mint
• Fennel	• Oregano
• Juniper	• Savory

• Another massage oil that helps in cases of flatulence is prepared from 10 ml. of sweet almond oil, 6 drops of chamomile, and 6 of ginger or mint. If you like, you can also prepare it with 6 drops of cardamom, or with 6 of fennel and 4 of mint.

Gout

Description

Gout is very painful; it is caused by an excess of uric acid in the blood. If the body is not well cleansed of toxins, they continue to accumulate and this is what happens with this illness.

The uric acid crystalizes and accumulates in the joints, causing pain and inflammation. The most commonly affected area for men is the big toe and for women, the shoulders.

Although diet has a big influence, it is also certain that nervous tension can trigger a crisis.

Aromatherapy remedies

● Warm footbaths give good results. Add one drop of pine, rosemary, juniper, cajuput, niaouli, or tea tree, and in ten minutes you will find that you feel a lot better.

Recommended essential oils

● Cajeput	● Niaouli
● Chamomile	● Pine
● Frankincense	● Rosemary
● Juniper	● Tea tree
● Lavender	● Thyme

● You can also massage the big toe with an undiluted drop of any of the recommended essential oils.
● Likewise, you can have a massage with a little bit of grape seed oil to which a drop of frankincense and another of lavender has been added.

Hay fever

Description

One of the most common forms of allergy is manifest as hay fever or rhinitis. Despite the name, it is not only caused by hay, but by any natural or chemical allergen (pollen, dust mites, animal dander, chemicals, food, etc.) or even by rhinitis vasomotor, which is to say, a non-allergic origin.

It is an affliction that causes inflammation of the nasal mucosa, and it can also affect the eyes, palate, and throat. The symptoms are bursts of sneezing, nasal congestion, watery eyes, headache, dry cough, fatigue, and irritability.

It can be treated with antihistamines or steroids, and there are people who undergo long treatments of vaccines in order to become desensitized to the allergens that produce this annoying affliction.

Natural medicine offers many alternatives and among them, aromatherapy. However, each one has a particular effect on the person, so it is advisable to test the recommended oils until you find the one that is most effective. The ideal would be to find

two or three that can be used together so as to reap the benefits of their synergy.

Recommended essential oils

● Basil	● Lavender
● Black Pepper	● Marjoram
● Cajeput	● Melissa
● Chamomile	● Mint
● Clary Sage	● Myrrh
● Clove	● Niaouli
● Eucalyptus	● Pine
● Hyssop	● Tea Tree
● Ginger	● Thyme

Aromatherapy remedies

● Add 10 drops of one of the recommended essential oils to bath water.
● Also you can put a number of drops of one of them on a handkerchief and sniff it. In addition, you can use a diffusor to achieve the same effect throughout your home.
● In 5 ml. of Vaseline, mix 2 or 3 drops of rose, chamomile, and/or lavender. When you have irritation or inflammation of the mucosa, apply it to the

nostrils two or three times a day.

• For irritated, runny eyes apply hot compresses of rose water. It would also be beneficial to massage the neck, the chest, and the back with 25 ml. of grape seed oil to which have been added 5 drops of chamomile or lavender, and 3 of melissa or rose. This can help to reduce the frequency and severity of the attack.

Headache

Description

The causes for the pain of headaches can vary considerably. They can often be caused by anxiety or eyestrain. Also, fever, mental fatigue, colds, sunstroke, digestive disorders (among these most headaches are related to constipation), and sinusitis are common causes of this nuisance that affects millions of people worldwide. Moreover, in women they can be attributed to hormonal changes that occur each month.

Aromatherapy remedies

• To combat troublesome headaches it is very beneficial to massage the temples (with special attention to the area around eyes) and the nape of the neck, since headaches are often caused by prolonged bad posture in front of the computer. Essential oils can contribute to relaxing and reducing inflammation in the area. For this, mix into 5 ml. of grape seed oil, one drop of basil, juniper, eucalyptus, chamomile, mint, lavender, marjoram, melissa, rosemary, or clary sage. Putting a few drops of rose, lavender, or melissa on a handkerchief and inhaling it directly can also bring relief.

• If the reason for the headache is eyestrain, soak a compress in water to which has been added a drop of chamomile, rose, lavender or rosemary. Keep in mind that you have to add the drop to the water in which the compress is soaked; the essential oil is not applied directly on the delicate skin of the eyelid, since it can be a major irritant if it comes in contact with your eyes. Lie down in a dark room and try to relax.

Recommended essential oils

- Angelica
- Basil
- Black Pepper
- Cajeput
- Chamomile
- Clary Sage
- Eucalyptus
- Geranium
- Frankincense
- Juniper
- Lavender
- Lemongrass
- Lemon
- Melissa
- Marjoram
- Mint
- Niaouli
- Rosemary
- Rose
- Tea Tree

• If the headache is caused by a sinus infection or a cold, the best thing is to make inhalations with hot water and a few drops of tea tree, eucalyptus, mint, marjoram, cajuput, geranium, or niaouli.

• When the reason is a hangover, opt for a long hot bath with a few drops of black pepper or juniper.

• You can also put a few drops of essential oil in a diffusor and lie down in your room for a while.

• If you want to clear your head, use angelica, juniper, eucalyptus, lemongrass, or rosemary. If you need to relieve pain and relax, the best are lavender, Roman

chamomile, rosemary, rose, and marjoram. In case you need to reduce nervous tension, opt for melissa, frankincense, or clary sage.

Hemorrhoids

Description

The veins that run through the lining of the anus may swell or become varicose and are then called "hemorrhoids" or "piles." The inflammation is usually the result of pressure imposed on the muscles of the abdomen by heavy lifting, constipation, being sedentary or overweight, or pregnancy. The veins can swell inside or outside, and become bloody, painful, and itchy. Although aromatherapy offers solutions, it is always advisable to consult a doctor if they are chronic or emerge bloody from the anus, because this could be a symptom of a different illness of the utmost gravity.

Aromatherapy remedies

● To prevent and alleviate symptoms, mix 25 ml. of calendula cream with 5 or 6 drops of cypress or yarrow and geranium. Apply the unguent as many times a day as needed.

● Also you can take seated baths with fresh water and 10 drops of any of the essential oils on the recommended list.

Recommended essential oils

● Bergamot	● Myrrh
● Chamomile	● Neroli
● Cypress	● Niaouli
● Geranium	● Patchouli
● Fennel	● Rosemary
● Frankincense	● Sandalwood
● Juniper	● Tea Tree
● Lemon	● Yarrow
● Marjoram	

Impotence

Description

The cases of impotence that require medical attention are few. In the majority of cases, the cause is psychological.

Aromatherapy helps to combat some psychological problems that have sexual dysfunction as a consequence, such as depression, stress, or nervous tension. In addition, it also provides some aphrodisiacs whose properties, although difficult to prove scientifically, are pleasant to discover.

Aromatherapy remedies

● A perfumed bath with ylang ylang and savory essential oils may be very stimulating, although any of the ones mentioned on the list can have a gentle aphrodisiac effect.

Recommended essential oils

● Cardamom	● Neroli
● Cedar	● Patchouli
● Celery	● Rosemary
● Clary Sage	● Rosewood
● Coriander	● Savory
● Ginger	● Thyme
● Jasmine	● Ylang Ylang
● Lavender	

● Massage is an excellent way to segue from a caress to pleasant and satisfactory sexual relations. Mix 50 ml. of grape seed oil with 5 drops of rose, sandalwood, and ylang ylang. The massage can be much more stimulating, if it is given by both members of the couple.

● You can also add a touch of aphrodisiac to the environment if you put any of the essential oils in an essence diffusor. A soft light, and let yourself go, just the ambience for the perfect starting point.

Influenza

Description

Influenza is a viral infection and is usually one of the main causes of fever.

Although several viruses can cause it, the symptoms, which last from three days to a week, are always similar: high fever, fatigue, respiratory tract infection, sore throat, cramps, and pain in the joints, back, and head.

It usually occurs every winter as an epidemic, and the elderly are at greatest risk, especially if they have cardiac or respiratory disorders. Every year there is usually a vaccination drive to prevent contagion, but it is not always effective, since the virus mutates and is often very resistant.

There is no cure for influenza, and all treatments are palliative. Aromatherapy offers solutions that are efficacious, natural, and pleasant at the same time.

Recommended essential oils

- Basil
- Bergamot
- Black Pepper
- Cajeput
- Camphor
- Ceylon Cinnamon
- Citronella
- Chamomile
- Clary Sage
- Clove
- Eucalyptus
- Ginger
- Lavender
- Lemongrass
- Lemon
- Marjoram
- Mint
- Palmarosa
- Tea Tree
- Thyme
- Yarrow

The most effective essential oil in this case is tea tree on account of its antiviral, bactericide, and immunostimulatory properties. In addition, it helps the body to sweat and regulate the temperature, which makes it useful for reducing fever.

Aromatherapy remedies

● At the first symptom of influenza, take a hot bath to which has been added 8 to 10 drops of tea tree and go straight to bed when you are done. Repeat the bath on the following nights, and it is possible that you will avoid becoming ill. If you add lavender, marjoram, or chamomile, this can also help you to alleviate general malaise and have a restorative night of sleep.

● Twice daily massage the nape of the neck, the chest, and the soles of the feet with 25 ml. of sweet almond oil and 4 drops of tea tree, eucalyptus, and cinnamon or clove.

● Nasal and chest congestion can be relieved with inhalations of hot water with niaouli, tea tree, and eucalyptus essential oil. If you put a few drops of marjoram or bergamot on your pillow, it will help you to sleep better.

● If you have the complication of a respiratory infection, add 2 or 3 drops of tea tree, clary sage, and thyme to a glass of hot water, mix it well, and gargle a couple of times a day.

● Influenza is very contagious, and it is advisable to cleanse the environment of the virus and germs. In an

essence diffusor put some drops of palmarosa, tea tree, rosemary, or black pepper.

Insomnia

Description

This word is of Latin origin that means absence of sleep. It is a malady that afflicts many people today on account of the anxiety, nervous tension, and stress that accompanies the rhythm of daily life. Pregnancy, premenstrual syndrome, and menopause can also cause insomnia, and it is more common as we grow older, because the older we get, the less sleep we need.

Exercise, maintaining an adequate diet, following a routine before going to bed, quitting smoking, and abstaining from alcohol and stimulant drinks, are some of the tools we can use to help us sleep better.

In addition, aromatherapy also helps naturally through essential oils with soothing, sedative, and hypnotic properties. Massages, essences diffusors, and a few drops on the pillow are some of the more common forms of application.

Aromatherapy remedies

● Put a few drops of lavender, rose, or mandarin essential oil on your pillow, and their aroma will help you fall asleep. You can also put an essence diffusor in your room half an hour before you go to sleep. You can use any of the recommended essential oils or create a combination until you find the aroma that makes you relax the most.

● Mix 10 ml. of sweet almond oil, 2 drops of neroli, melissa, petitgrain, clary sage, or lavender and have a gentle and relaxing massage in bed, ideally before you go to sleep.

● A hot bath before sleeping is relaxing in itself, but the effect can be enhanced if you add 10 drops of marjoram, chamomile, melissa, rose or lavender, or a combination of various ones. Breathe deeply and calmly during the bath, which should not exceed 10 minutes. And when you finish, go directly to bed.

● A nice and pleasant trick consists of adding 10 drops of the essential oil that you like the most to the water when you clean the sheets so that they become impregnated with the aroma, which will help you fall asleep. You can also place floral sachets filled with dried lavender in your linen closet (remember that you have to replace it frequently) or soak your clothing in a few drops of lavender essential oil.

Recommended essential oils

- Basil
- Chamomile
- Clary Sage
- Cypress
- Juniper
- Lavender
- Lemon
- Mandarin
- Marjoram
- Melissa
- Neroli
- Petitgrain
- Sandalwood
- Vetiver
- Ylang Ylang

Intestinal colic

Description

Intestinal colic is a sharp pain in the belly caused by fermentation of certain foods in the intestine, such as cheese or other dairy products. It can also result from a strong intestinal flu or a food intolerance.

Intestinal colic occurring in babies is due to the fact that the bowel is still immature and does not digest the small pockets of air swallowed by the child when breastfeeding or being bottle fed. This is called "infantile," or "baby colic." On the other hand, to ensure that it is not an inflammatory reaction, you should rule out lactose intolerance.

Aromatherapy remedies

● For colic in children, it is highly recommended to massage the belly with a gentle, circular motion in a clockwise direction with 50 ml. of sweet almond oil, 2 drops of wheat germ oil, and 12 drops of caraway. You should warm the massage oil slightly before applying it. It is sufficient to simply hold the bottle under warm running water.

● Another massage oil especially recommended for children is made by adding 2 drops of marjoram and roman chamomile to 60 ml. of sweet almond oil. Then, proceed as in the same way.

Recommended essential oils

● Angelica	● Juniper
● Bergamot	● Lavender
● Black Pepper	● Marjoram
● Caraway	● Melissa
● Cardamom	● Mint
● Carrot	● Orange
● Chamomile	● Neroli
● Clary Sage	● Oregano
● Clove	● Petitgrain
● Fennel	● Pine
● Hyssop	● Yarrow

● It is important that the baby not be nervous. For this, you can place cotton soaked in pine and orange, or lavender and orange, on the radiator in the room. This will create a relaxed atmosphere.

● For adults, a massage oil can be made using any of the recommended oils on the list. It is important for the oil to be warm and applied to the belly in circular movements in a clockwise direction.

Leucorrhea

Description

What is known as "leucorrhea" is an inflammation of the vagina usually caused by bacteria, although it can also be caused by the fungus *Candida albicans*, and other species. The symptoms are white or yellow fluid with a bad odor, redness, and moderate inflammation in the vaginal region, and intense, continual pruritus.

Its appearance often coincides with taking antibiotics, because the body is weak. The groups most at risk are women who are diabetic, taking birth control pills, or pregnant.

Recommended essential oils

● Eucalyptus	● Lavender
● Geranium	● Myrrh
● Juniper	● Tea Tree

- Seated baths are the most effective for combating leucorrhea.
- Fill a bidet (or bath) with hot water and add 2 drops of juniper, tea tree, or lavender. Take a ten-minute bath every day until the discomfort has disappeared.
- You can also take a hot bath to which have been added 8 to 10 drops of any of the recommended essential oils on the list.

Lumbago

Description

The lumbar area of the spine is situated on the base of the back and is usually susceptible to suffering from pinching, inflammation, or even herniated discs. The pain is commonly known as "lumbago" and is very disabling.

It tends to be caused by bad posture when lifting, twisting the spinal column, or carrying additional weight throughout the day, as is the case with pregnant women.

Recommended essential oils

Basil	Lavender
Black Pepper	Lemon
Cajeput	Niaouli
Chamomile	Oregano
Clary Sage	Pine
Ginger	Rosemary
Juniper	Thyme

The only way to soothe the pain and inflammation is to stay calm, apply heat, and massage the affected area.

Aromatherapy remedies

- Hot baths are very effective. Take 6 drops of oregano and 6 of thyme and a little bit of bath gel and put it under the faucet while filling the bathtub.
- Heat can also be applied locally with hot compresses soaked in water to which have been added 5 drops of juniper, pine, rosemary, or thyme. Leave it on for ten minutes and you will feel the relief. It can be repeated several times a day.

- A massage after applying heat is an excellent way to penetrate the pores of your skin with the active ingredients of the essential oils of your choice. Mix 10 ml. of sweet almond oil with 2 drops of wheat germ oil, and 6 drops of any of the recommended essential oils.

Menopause

Description

Menopause is the last phase of a woman's menstrual cycle.

For some women it is a difficult time, since it combines several physical and psychological factors that have a direct impact on the quality of life.

The hormonal change, which signifies a decrease in estrogen and progesterone production, can take years to completely occur.

During its course 25 percent of women experience dizziness, hot flashes, insomnia, headaches, irregular and heavy menses, depression, palpitations, irritability, sudden changes of mood, and fluid retention.

It's best to consider this a natural process and accept it in order to facilitate a smooth transition through the change.

Natural medicine can help in many ways and aromatherapy offers some very pleasant remedies.

Aromatherapy remedies

● Choose the essential oil that always makes you feel better and put a few drops in an essence diffusor. It will help you relax and calm your irritability, one of the main symptoms of menopause.

● Cold compresses with essential oil of chamomile, lavender, mint, or rose are very useful for hot flashes. Apply it to the face and body whenever you need it.

● A hot bath will make you feel much better, and it will be a time dedicated exclusively to yourself. Add a total of 8 or 10 drops of one or more of the recommended essential oils on the list. If you have night sweats, a good option is to take a lukewarm bath before bed with 5 drops of clary sage and 5 more of geranium.

● A massage will help you to feel better and relax you. Mix 15 ml. of orange or borage oil (highly recommended for its linoleic acid content) with 25 ml. of grape seed or 5 drops of geranium or rose, 5 of fennel, and 5 of clary sage. Their active ingredients will relax you and help to regulate your body, which becomes unbalanced during menopause.

● An oil to regulate hormones and soothe your symptoms can be made from 30 ml. of sweet almond oil, 2 drops of rose, 2 of sandalwood, 3 of cypress, and 3 of bitter orange.

Migraine

Description

Migraine is one of the most common afflictions of the nervous system. It consists of intense headaches that occur on a regular basis and cause considerable suffering, to the extent that they can be incapacitating while they last. They are caused by a sudden arterial spasm on one side of the head. The pain occurs when the arteries are reverting to a normal state. It seems that there might be a hereditary factor, but it has been shown that women suffer much more frequently from migraines than men.

The symptoms, which can last from a few hours to several days, consist of

a palpitating headache that can be accompanied by dizziness and vomiting. On occasion it affects the vision; one may see specks of light half an hour before an episode. This type of migraine is called a "migraine with aura." If remedial action is taken when you see these specks of light, you are more likely to prevent or soften the attack.

A healthy diet (avoiding cheese, chocolate, and wine), outdoor exercise, and living with less anxiety can improve the prospects of those who are prone to suffer from it. Aromatherapy can also help you to prevent it, lessen it, or fight it.

Aromatherapy remedies

● When you notice the first symptoms, one way to lessen the attack is to prepare an oil massage with 5 drops of grape seed oil and 1 drop of basil. Massage the neck and solar plexus in a circular motion, in a clockwise direction and lie in bed in the dark for as long as necessary. The massage can be repeated until the symptoms disappear. If the pain does not permit the affected area to be touched, you can inhale the va-

pors of essential oil or pour some onto a handkerchief.

● Another efficacious remedy to apply when you have the first symptoms is to pour 2 drops of marjoram, 2 of lavender, 2 of mint, and 1 of melissa onto a handkerchief. Inhale deeply three times in order to get the proper effect.

● It can be helpful to put any of the recommended essential oils into an essence diffusor or 8 drops in hot bath water.

Neuralgia

Description

Neuralgia is defined as any pain caused by irritation or compression of a nerve, such as herpes zoster, sciatica, or trigeminal pain. Its cause may be any inflammation, infection, or compression caused by a fracture, a herniated disc, a headache, a sinus infection, or a toothache. Among the best-known neuralgias are migraine, sciatica, and facial neuralgia. The last responds very well to aromatherapy.

Aromatherapy remedies

● Pour on a handkerchief 1 drop of tea tree, niaouli, or eucalyptus, and take three deep breaths.

● Warm compresses with a few drops of any of the previously mentioned essential oils, give good results for facial neuralgia.

● An analgesic massage oil can be made with 5 drops of grape seed essential oil, 2 drops of wheat germ oil, and 3 of black pepper.

● For neuralgias in the rest of the body, beneficial results can be obtained with a warm handkerchief to which have been added 8 to 10 drops of any of the recommended essential oils.

● A very suitable massage oil for pain relief is made from 50 ml. of hypericum-infused oil and 25 drops in total of rosemary, lavender, marjoram, and/or mint. Gently massage the affected area so that it penetrates well.

Pediculosis (lice)

Description

Pediculosis refers to three types of insect: body lice, head lice, and crabs (or pubic lice). In all three cases, the infestation occurs very quickly and is always from contact with other people. These undesirable insects pierce the skin to suck blood. These miniscule wounds itch and produce extreme irritation.

Aromatherapy remedies

- As a preventative measure, before washing your hair, add 2 drops of lavender or tea tree essential oil to shampoo. The following may also be added to a bottle of shampoo: for every 100 ml. of neutral shampoo, add 20, 40, or 60 drops of essential oil (depending on whether it is for children, if you have sensitive skin, or if it is for adults). Leave it on for ten minutes and rinse your hair thoroughly. To finish, you can also add 2 drops of lavender essential oil to the conditioner or water for the last rinse.

- **Hair lice**: rub the scalp with an alcohol remedy, such as rosemary alcohol, to which have been added 10 drops of any of the three essential oils that we propose. Leave it on overnight and in the morning comb the hair to with a special comb for removing lice and nits (eggs). If desired, repeat the treatment for three consecutive nights. If you irritate the scalp as a result of the alcohol, you can substitute sweet almond oil or oil infused with rosemary.

- What works well for children is to apply for half an hour a mixture of 10 ml. of sweet almond oil, 2 drops of eucalyptus, 1 of lavender, and 1 of geranium. Afterwards wash the hair and apply an antiseptic mixture that should be left on all night: 240 ml. of water, 15 ml. of vinegar, 2 drops of eucalyptus, 2 of lavender, and 2 of geranium. In the morning, comb it with the special comb, after having washed the hair again. It is also very useful to add this mixture to the water of the last rinse as preventive a measure against future contagions or relapses.

- **Body Lice:** Use the previous solution and rub it all over your body. Change the sheets, put on a protective cover, clean the mattress, and rub it with lavender essential oil.

- **Crabs:** as a first step you should shave your pubic hair and then apply the same mixture, but being careful not to let it enter the body through the urethra, anus or vagina.

Pneumonia

Description

When suffering from pneumonia, an infection of the lung, the alveoli become inflamed as a result of being attacked by bacteria or a virus and are filled with pus and mucus.

Pneumonia can also result from an irritation caused by certain chemical agents, severe bronchitis, or even flu that is not well cured.

Pneumonia does not always have warning signs, and the symptoms can range from very mild to very severe: fever, difficulty breathing, chest pain, chills, a dry, persistent cough, and bloody sputum. If you suspect that you have pneumonia, you should consult a doctor; you will need a strong antibiotic treatment in order to overcome it. This disease can be serious when it comes to children, people with respiratory problems, or the elderly.

Aromatherapy is, in this case, a complementary medicine that facilitates a faster and more complete recovery, but it does not have the ability to cure this infection.

Aromatherapy remedies

● Prevention is one of the best medicines for avoiding pneumonia. To do this, put 3 drops of tea tree, eucalyptus, or cajuput essential oil in a diffusor to clear the air in your home of threatening bacteria and viruses. If any family members have pneumonia, this will prevent others from contagion.

● It is also highly recommended that you practice inhalations for chest congestion. To do this, put a few drops of pine or cypress in hot water and breathe deeply.

Recommended essential oils

● Cajeput	● Oregano
● Cedar	● Pine
● Cypress	● Rosemary
● Eucalyptus	● Tea Tree
● Niaouli	● Thyme

● The application of hot compresses can also bring relief. Soak the compress in hot water to which have been added 2 drops of oregano and apply it to the chest. Leave it on for ten minutes and then get a gentle massage with 15 ml. of sweet almond oil, 2 drops of wheat germ oil, 2 of cedar, 2 of cajuput, and 3 of eucalyptus. When finished, cover the chest well.

● Apply 2 drops of rosemary, thyme, or tea tree on the soles of the feet and hands in the morning and evening.

Pregnancy

Description

It is quite normal to feel various discomforts associated with pregnancy. And some essential oils can be of great help during the entire period of pregnancy and childbirth. However, there are others that you can use only from the fourth month of pregnancy and others that you should avoid completely because they regulate the menstrual cycle, or raise blood pressure.

In the description of the essential oils given in this book we provide warnings in order to prevent you from making mistakes. However, there is no doubt that those essential oils that are beneficial during pregnancy and the months following delivery are wonderful natural restoratives, and can help you to overcome the typical inconveniences of pregnancy and contribute to your wellbeing. You can use them in a diffusor or bath or as a massage oil, always diluted to half the usual dose, but the massage should only be given from the fifth month of pregnancy.

We recommend, in all cases, to follow the advice of an expert aromatherapist, whom you trust.

Aromatherapy remedies

● You can prevent the appearance of unsightly stretch marks if you gently massage the belly and breasts in the morning and in the evening. It is important to wait until very late in the fourth month before starting. Mix 15 ml. of sweet almond oil, 15 ml. of wheat germ oil, and 25 ml. of jojoba. Then add up to a maximum of 10 drops of a combination of various essential oils such as rose, neroli, frankincense, and lavender, or only one if you prefer.

● A great solution for when you are tired and sore, especially at the end of the pregnancy, is to take a hot bath to which have been added 4 to 5 drops of any of the essential oils that we recommend. The ones that give the best results are lavender and chamomile, which can be added in equal parts.

● To soothe kidney pain, anxiety, fatigue, or postpartum depression rose, neroli, petitgrain, lavender, and chamomile can be of great help. Mix 50 ml. of almond oil, 5 drops of wheat germ oil, and 10 to 12 drops of any of these essential oils. If you suffer from postpartum depression, you can use bergamot, neroli, lavender, mandarin, rose, vetiver, and even ylang ylang. You can apply a couple of drops as if it were your favorite perfume or, if you prefer, place them in a diffusor.

● A very refreshing remedy if your last months of pregnancy coincide with the summer is to apply compresses that have been soaked in very cold water with a few drops of lavender or chamomile. The floral waters of these essential oils are also a great help, and you can spray them on your face during the hot days of summer as often as you like.

Oils prohibited during pregnancy

- Angelica
- Basil
- Birch
- Carrot
- Celery
- Ceylon Cinnamon
- Cedar
- Citronella
- Clary Sage
- Clove
- Cypress
- Fennel
- Hyssop
- Juniper
- Marjoram
- Melissa
- Myrrh
- Oregano
- Pine
- Savory
- Thyme
- White Camphor
- Yarrow

Recommended throughout the entire pregnancy

- Bergamot
- Caraway
- Cardamom
- Chamomile
- Frankincense
- Geranium
- Ginger
- Grapefruit
- Lavender
- Mandarin
- Orange (bitter)
- Orange (sweet)
- Neroli
- Patchouli
- Sandalwood
- Vetiver

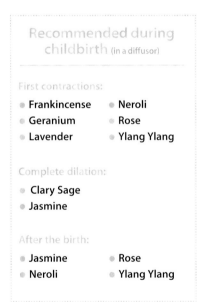

Premenstrual Syndrome

Description

Premenstrual syndrome is a set of symptoms that occur several days before menstruation, such as breast tenderness, headache, mood swings, fluid retention, constipation, and insomnia, among others. There are many women who suffer from it, and there are many types of premenstrual syndrome, since in every woman it appears in different, and sometimes multiple, forms.

Its seems to be due to a hormonal imbalance between the levels of estrogen and progesterone that occurs at the time of the menstrual cycle, but there still remains much to learn about the reasons for and consequences of this syndrome. This is because the brain, through the hypothalamus and the pituitary gland, directs the hormonal concert that takes place each cycle.

In addition, external factors, such as stress or depression, have a direct effect on it. Meanwhile many women are left to cope as best they can with this monthly ordeal.

Aromatherapy is very useful in the treatment of premenstrual syndrome because it can have an impact on physical factors, such as fluid retention, and on psychological ones, such as anxiety or mood swings.

Moreover, since is a very pleasant therapy, it creates an implicit sensation of pampering oneself, which always helps one to cope with difficult situations.

Aromatherapy remedies

- Warm baths are a great help during these days. Add 10 drops of the essential oil that you like the most from the recommended list ten days before, and if there is still discomfort, continue during menstruation.

- Massage helps one to relax and is a great way to get the active ingredients of essential oils to reach their destination quickly. Prepare a mixture in accordance with the symptoms. For example, if you suffer from mood swings and get very irritable, add 15 ml. of evening primrose oil and 50 ml. of grape seed oil, 10 drops of lavender, bergamot, geranium, and chamomile.

- As a preventive measure, you can bring your body into hormonal balance with a massage. Mix 25 ml. of grape seed oil and 15 ml. of evening primrose oil with 5 drops of rose, lavender, fennel, and geranium. Massage the belly and the lower back.

● Essence diffusors can help with anxiety and soothe the symptoms of premenstrual syndrome. Use one or more of the oils chosen for the ten days preceding menstruation.

Recommended essential oils

● Basil	● Melissa
● Bergamot	● Neroli
● Chamomile	● Patchouli
● Clary Sage	● Palmarosa
● Cypress	● Pine
● Geranium	● Rosemary
● Grapefruit	● Rose
● Fennel	● Sandalwood
● Frankincense	● Tarragon
● Jasmine	● Thyme
● Juniper	● Vetiver
● Lemon	● Ylang Ylang
● Mandarin	

Psoriasis
Description

This disease of unknown origin (some argue that it is hereditary) manifests as pink or reddish circular spots on the skin. It usually begins by appearing on the elbows and knees and then can spread throughout the body. The affected skin is usually very dry and scaly. The affliction is virtually incurable, but it responds well to treatment with aromatherapy.

It is best to avoid humid climates. Cold and nervous tension are other factors that worsen psoriasis.

Aromatherapy remedies

● If blemishes appear on the face, apply wheat germ oil, which will keep the skin clean and moisturized.

● When it appears on the scalp, you can apply 5 ml. of castor oil with 2 drops of wheat germ oil, and 4 drops of benzoin or cajuput. Gently massage your head and wrap it in a warm towel to promote absorption of the active ingredients of the essential oil. After two hours, wash your head with a very neutral shampoo. Do not use a dryer.

● Morning and night apply a mixture on the blemishes containing 10 ml. of wheat germ oil and 3 drops of benzoin or cajuput. If after two months you do not note an improvement, try it with another of the recommended essential oils.

Recommended essential oils

● Angelica	● Lemon
● Benzoin	● Myrrh
● Cajeput	● Oregano
● Cedar	● Tea Tree
● Lavender	● Thyme

● Another treatment that can help consists of 25 ml. of avocado oil, 25 ml. of evening primrose oil, 5 drops of wheat germ oil, 15 drops of tea tree, and 5 more of myrrh or cajuput. Apply twice a day to the affected area.

● Also beneficial are warm baths to which have been added salts from the Dead Sea and a few drops of any of the recommended essential oils.

Rheumatism
Description

The term "rheumatism" refers to several diseases that affect the tissue of the joints, such as arthritis or bursitis, among others. Sometimes the tissue, ligament, tendon, or muscle becomes rigid, and other times it just swells and is painful. What is definite is that it causes

pain and can reduce mobility and, therefore, the quality of life.

Aromatherapy is a great help for reducing inflammation and relieving pain, and consequently improving mobility and the quality of life. There are many essential oils that can help, and it is likely that some will be more effective for you than others. If you want to test the long list that we offer seek advice from an aromatherapist you trust.

Aromatherapy remedies

● Mix 10 ml. of grape seed essential oil with 2 drops of cajuput, or 1 drop of pine and 1 of lemon or juniper. Have a long but gentle massage in the affected area, and cover it afterward with a warm towel. Thus the active ingredients penetrate better and help the stiff joints extend.

● Another massage oil that very effectively reduces inflammation is infused with hypericum. Mix 25 ml. with 3 or 4 drops of lavender, juniper, rosemary, and black pepper or ginger. In addition, the massage stimulates blood circulation and helps to eliminate toxins that are harmful for people with rheumatic diseases.

Recommended essential oils

- Angelica
- Black Pepper
- Cajeput
- Carrot
- Citronella
- Chamomile
- Clary sage
- Clove
- Coriander
- Cypress
- Eucalyptus
- Ginger
- Hyssop
- Juniper
- Laurel
- Lavender
- Lemon
- Lime
- Niaouli
- Oregano
- Petitgrain
- Pine
- Thyme
- Vetiver
- White Birch

● Hot baths also alleviate pain while reducing inflammation and detoxifying. Add 8 to 10 drops of any of the recommended essential oils or combine those that you like, but never more than three or four different ones each time.

● If you have pain in a certain area, you can apply a compress soaked in warm water with 2 drops of lavender, 2 of rosemary, 3 of eucalyptus, 2 of cajuput or chamomile, and 3 more of juniper. Place it on the area and leave it on overnight.

Sciatica

Description

Sciatic pain is produced by an inflammation of the sciatic nerve and can extend from the lower part of the back to the outside of the thigh, through the buttocks. This inflammation is usually caused by pressure from a vertebra on the nerve, which can be brought on by a sudden movement, lifting a weight, twisting, or after childbirth. Aromatherapy relaxes the muscles and relieves the pain.

Aromatherapy remedies

● Mix 15 ml. of grape seed oil with 2 drops of any of the recommended essential oils on the list provided. Gently massage the painful areas and keep them warm while applying heat locally with a blanket, for example. Taking a hot bath to

Recommended essential oils

- Angelica
- Black Pepper
- Celery
- Mint
- Oregano
- Sandalwood
- Thyme

which have been added a few drops of the recommended essential oils also brings relief.

Sinusitis

Description

Sinusitis is an infection of the nose and paranasal sinuses, or the cavities around the nose and eyes. It is a common health problem and one that is also quite painful.

The most common symptoms are headache, nasal congestion, fatigue, soreness around the eyes, coughing, and fever. It may even cause nosebleeds due to the pressure exerted by inflamed sinuses as a result of inflammation.

This disease usually originates from a poorly healed ailment of the upper respiratory tract, such as flu, cold, sore throat, or oral infection. It can also be a symptom of hay fever.

Aromatherapy remedies

● Inhalations are a great help, especially decongestant and anti-inflammatory essential oils such as eucalyptus, benzoin, rosemary, or cajeput. In addition, tea tree has powerful anti-septic properties that can help to overcome the infection. Perform inhalations three or four times a day with 4 drops of one or more of these essential oils.

● Take a bath daily with 10 drops of any of the oils listed above. It provides the same benefits as inhalations.

● An effective way to fight infection is to put into a diffusor or vaporizer a few drops of tea tree, eucalyptus and /or thyme during the day, and marjoram or lavender at night.

● Mix 5 ml. of vaseline, 1 drop of chamomile, 1 of lavender and 1 of rose. Apply it to the nostrils to try to reduce the inflammation of the mucous membranes and thereby facilitate respiration.

● To relieve congestion, massage the neck, chest, hands, and soles of the feet with 25 ml. of grape seed oil and 3 drops of eucalyptus, pine or rosemary, and mint.

● Every evening apply the following lotion on the face: 15 ml. of cream, 3 drops of lavender, 2 of mint, and 2 of eucalyptus.

● To make it most effective, perform the following massage: put your fingers in a vertical position with the thumbs supported under the jaw. Continue, pressing along the top of the cheekbones up to the temples. Then gently massage from the starting point and again perform the anterior movement but in the middle of the cheekbones.

Recommended essential oils

● **Benzoin**	● **Marjoram**
● **Bergamot**	● **Mint**
● **Cajeput**	● **Myrrh**
● **Chamomile**	● **Niaouli**
● **Clary Sage**	● **Pine**
● **Clove**	● **Rosemary**
● **Eucalyptus**	● **Rose**
● **Ginger**	● **Tea Tree**
● **Hyssop**	● **Thyme**
● **Lavender**	

Stress

Description

When you are under stress, in fact you are actually suffering from two conditions at the same time: physical and emotional. In itself stress is necessary for human beings, since the adrenaline that the body secretes maintains it in state of alertness when the occasion warrants it, such as for imminent danger or any situation that requires extreme attention.

The problem occurs when in daily life we are subjected to a continuous state of vigilance, either for personal or for professional reasons, and the reaction of the body continues for days, weeks, or even months. Then, the results on our mind and our body can become very serious: hypertension, nervous fatigue, digestive disorders, nervous anxiety, depression, headaches, insomnia, weakness of the immune system, and even predisposition to fatal diseases, such as heart disease or kidney failure.

Aromatherapy can help treat the multitude of symptoms of this "modern disease," but it is essential that treatment be accompanied by a few critical changes of habit. For example, exercising, if possible in the open air, helps to release physical and emotional stress. It is also a good idea to change one's approach to major problems, and to do things to control anxiety and not to demand the impossible. Yoga, deep breathing, meditation, or even the help of a psychotherapist, are some very useful tools for dealing with this important problem, so widespread in society.

Aromatherapy remedies

● A warm bath is a very effective way to relax. In addition, it will also help to add some drops of the recommended essential oils. In this way you can reduce tension and anxiety and have a restorative sleep.

● You can also rub some drops of lavender or chamomile mixed with 5 ml. of sweet almond oil on your hands and the soles of your feet. Do it in the morning and before going to sleep.

● An essence diffusor contributes to a relaxing environment. Burn some drops of lavender, frankincense, or bergamot, and if you like, add ylang ylang, neroli, or rose to perfume the room. You can also put a few drops on a handkerchief and sniff it from time to time.

Recommended essential oils

- Basil
- Bergamot
- Chamomile
- Frankincense
- Jasmine
- Lavender
- Mandarin
- Marjoram
- Melissa
- Orange (sweet)
- Neroli
- Petitgrain
- Rose
- Ylang Ylang

● It is very important to schedule a total body massage at least once a week. The massage oil can include sweet almond to which has been added drops of clary sage, ylang ylang, and lavender. You will feel a lot better.

Toothache

Description

This pain is caused by an infection familiar to all: cavities. When bacteria gets through the enamel and reaches the pulp, and then touches the nerve, pain begins, which can be very intense and persistent. If you have toothache you should go to your dentist right away, in order to get a filling or "kill" the nerve, so that the pain goes away. If the bacteria reach the bone where the affected tooth is inserted, you run a serious risk.

However, while are waiting for your dental appointment, aromatherapy can offer some emergency solutions to help you as much as possible during this period.

A healthy diet, good oral hygiene and visiting your dentist regularly can help to ensure that you will not have to suffer as painful a malady as a toothache can be.

Aromatherapy remedies

• You can apply cotton dipped in two drops of clove or mint essential oil when you go to the dentist since they have anesthetic and antiseptic properties.

• You can massage the outside of the cheek with 15 ml. of sweet almond oil, 2 drops of chamomile, 2 of lavender, and 2 of mint.

Recommended essential oils

● Angelica	● Lavender
● Black Pepper	● Mint
● Chamomile	● Myrrh
● Clove	● Tea Tree
● Coriander	● Thyme

• As a preventive measure and to combat infection, you can gargle each time after you brush your teeth with a glass of water to which have been added 5 drops of tea tree.

Varicose veins

Description

When there is bad circulation, blood running from the legs to the heart collects in the veins, which become swollen and twisted. These are varicose veins. They can also appear on other parts of the body, such as the anus or scrotum.

This disease can be due to various causes, such as pregnancy, constipation, spending many hours standing, or excess weight. The symptom is a dull, intense pain in the legs. In addition, the unsightliness bothers people who suffer from them.

Aromatherapy remedies

• At the end of the day, give yourself a gentle massage on the legs with 20 ml. of almond oil and 8 drops of cypress.

• Mix 25 ml. of jojoba oil with 2 drops of carrot, 1 of grapefruit, and 2 of fennel. Apply this thick cream on varicose veins and rub vigorously, taking care to allow it to penetrate.

• Another beneficial body massage is 50 ml. of grape seed oil, 8 drops of rosemary, 8 of geranium and 8 of fennel.

• Baths should be warm, because heat dilates the veins and increases blood flow. Add 10 drops of any or several of the previously mentioned essential oils and remain for not more than ten minutes. In the shower, you can add a couple of drops of any of them to the sponge and gently rub the legs in an upward circular motion.

• Another mixture that works well for massaging your aching legs is made from 30 ml. of grape seed oil, 3 drops of cypress, 2 of sandalwood, and 1 of mint. In this case, it is better not to press directly on varicose veins. It is preferable to massage them with your palms.

Recommended essential oils

● Angelica	● Lavender
● Bergamot	● Lemon
● Carrot	● Lime
● Celery	● Mandarin
● Clary Sage	● Marjoram
● Coriander	● Orange
● Cypress	● Petitgrain
● Fennel	● Rosemary
● Geranium	● Tea Tree
● Grapefruit	● Yarrow
● Juniper	

First aid

Cuts and wounds

Recommended
essential oils

- Benzoin
- Black Pepper
- Chamomile
- Clary sage
- Eucalyptus
- Geranium
- Hyssop
- Lavender
- Palmarosa
- Rosemary
- Rosa
- Savory
- Tea Tree

Aromatherapy remedies

- Add a drop of tea tree, eucalyptus, geranium, or clary sage essential oil to warm water, and use it to thoroughly wash the cut or wound.
- Essential oils that provide the best cure are chamomile, geranium, lavender, palmarosa, and eucalyptus. Those that promote good healing are chamomile, geranium, and black pepper.
- If there is a scar on your face, rose is the best essential oil to use.

Hematomas

Recommended
essential oils

- Clary Sage
- Cypress
- Fennel
- Geranium
- Lavender
- Marjoram
- Mint
- Rosemary

Aromatherapy remedies

- After applying a drop of geranium or lavender on the hematoma, the best follow up is to apply a cold compress with any of the recommended essential oils.
- If the hematoma turns a greenish yellow, it is good to massage it with a carrier oil that has a few drops of clary sage, fennel, or rosemary, since all of these promote circulation.
- In the case of multiple bruises resulting from a fall or accident, prepare a hot bath with 10 drops of marjoram or geranium.

Insect bites

Recommended
essential oils

- Basil
- Citronella
- Fennel
- Geranium
- Lavender
- Melissa
- Niaouli
- Oregano
- Tea Tree
- Thyme

Aromatherapy remedies

- Insect bites can become truly annoying. To soothe them, you can apply a drop of lavender or tea tree directly on the wounded area.
- Citronella and melissa are very soothing oils and can be applied directly on the bite.
- The rest of the oils can be applied with a cold compress if you have multiple bites, as is often the case with mosquito bites.

Insect repellent

Recommended essential oils

- Basil
- Bergamot
- Cedar
- Citronella
- Cypress
- Eucalyptus
- Geranium
- Lavender
- Lemongrass
- Lemon
- Niaouli
- Rosewood
- Vetiver

Aromatherapy remedies

- An essence diffusor is the simplest insect repellent there is. Put in a few drops of one or more of the recommended oils and it will keep the mosquitoes away.
- You can also add 10 drops of one of these essential oils to the bath to make your skin smell of its aroma and insects will not approach you. Choose the one you like to perfume yourself and repel insects.

Minor burns

Recommended essential oils

- Benzoin
- Chamomile
- Clary Sage
- Eucalyptus
- Geranium
- Lavender
- Niaouli
- Patchouli
- Rose
- Tea Tree

Aromatherapy remedies

- Immediately after a minor burn, immerse the injured area in cold water, and then apply a cold compress, so that the affected area is cool and stays clean, after applying a drop of lavender or tea tree essential oil.
- After having carried out the first procedure, you can soak a compress in cold water with some of the other oils we propose and apply it on the burn.

Sunburn

Recommended essential oils

- Cedar
- Chamomile
- Cypress
- Eucalyptus
- Geranium
- Jasmine
- Lavender
- Neroli
- Niaouli
- Patchouli
- Rosewood
- Rose
- Sandalwood
- Tea Tree

Aromatherapy remedies

- An ideal lotion after sunbathing, if you have not suffered any burns, consists of 25 ml. of sweet almond oil, 2 drops of wheat germ oil, 2 drops of lavender, 2 of rosewood, and 2 of geranium.
- The best way to relieve pain and itching caused by sunburn is to apply one or more of these essential oils in a compress with very cold water.

Essential oils for the soul

Aromatherapy remedies for your emotions

Here we offer some suggestions to help you feel better in your most difficult times. People are body, mind and emotions. And there is no doubt that all three elements are very closely related. Therefore aromatherapy, in addition to providing solutions for physical ailments, also seeks to relieve the problems generated by our innermost self.

Negative emotions can have an impact on our body. We need to be responsible for our own health and vital balance, so we need to give the same attention to the inner being as to the physical body.

A long list that can be made of negative states of mind, but essential oils can help you regain optimism, self-confidence, and the drive to tackle difficult situations.

Below, we offer some examples of these emotions and the essential oils that are useful in each case.

As we are dealing with subjective states, the choice of which oils to use has to be personal one. It is good to try various blends and remedies, either with the advice of your aromatherapist or on your own initiative.

We will make some suggestions of the main, effective ways to apply aromatherapy to the symptoms that produce your emotions, but you choose the rest.

In any event, a hint: lavender, mandarin and, above all, rose are the essential oils that give the best results when it comes to feeling better. Although these do not in the least exclude the rest of the essential oils that we suggest.

Inhaling essences from a handkerchief

● **If you suddenly feel anxiety, sadness, or nervousness,** for example, as a result of an upset or stressful situation, pour 4 drops of lavender on a handkerchief and inhale deeply.

● **All the essential oils** that we suggest for each emotion can help if you carry a handkerchief with a few drops and inhale deeply the moment you feel a particular negative emotion.

A restorative bath

● **A hot bath is in itself a good way** to combat negative emotional states. If you add 10 drops of any of the oils recommended for emotions in the following section, it will become quite a therapeutic remedy. A very effective, soothing blend consists of 2 drops of geranium, 2 of lavender, 2 of sandalwood, and 1 of ylang ylang.

● **It is claimed that rose essential oil is the most emotionally therapeutic in a bath.**

● **Depending on the negative emotion** you have, add 2 drops of the appropriate essential oil to the bath gel that you put on a sponge during your morning shower.

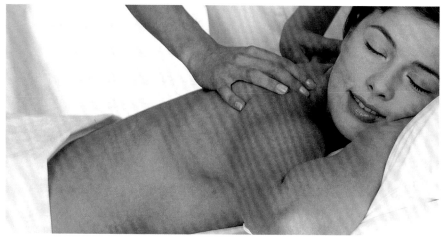

A comforting massage

● **Ask someone to give you a massage** in a peaceful and relaxing atmosphere with the following oil: 15 ml. of grape seed oil, 2 drops of rose, 2 of lavender, 2 of sandalwood, and 2 of bergamot. It will restore your serenity, and you will be able to face your problems with renewed energy.

● **This essential oil blend is very soothing:** 50 ml. of sweet almond oil, 8 drops of clary sage, 8 of ylang ylang, and 8 of lavender.

● **If stress is taking its toll on your mood,** mix 5 ml. of sweet almond oil with 2 or 3 drops of chamomile or lavender and use your hands to rub it on the soles of the feet. If anxiety grips your stomach, massage the solar plexus in a circular, clockwise direction.

● **For only one massage,** add 15 ml. of sweet almond oil, 2 drops of rose, and 2 of melissa. It will

Aromatherapy has also sought to offer relief for the problems created by our innermost self.

help you regain tranquility.

Perfume your soul

● **Lavender, frankincense, bergamot, and rose** are some of the most effective options for a diffusor, but there are dozens of possibilities. A few drops are enough to scent the rooms in your home and create a relaxing ambience full of harmony.

● **If you suffer from anxiety,** we recommend using neroli, rose or ylang ylang.

Self-massage: simple and effective

● **Mix 5 ml. of sweet almond oil** with 2 or 3 drops of lime or rosemary and using your hands, rub the soles of your feet. This massage recharges your energy, renews your strength helps you persevere through difficulties.

● **You can also mix 5 ml. of grape seed oil** with 2 drops of cypress or melissa, rub on your hands and the soles of the feet. If anxiety grips your stomach, massage the solar plexus in a circular, clockwise motion.

● **For jealousy or envy,** take 5 ml. of sweet almond oil, 2 drops of rose or lavender and rub the hands, soles of the feet, and the solar plexus.

Essential oils for negative emotions

Anger
- Bergamot
- Cedar
- Chamomile
- Frankincense
- Lavender
- Lemon
- Mandarin
- Marjoram
- Melissa
- Mint
- Myrrh
- Orange (bitter)
- Petitgrain
- Rose
- Sandalwood
- Ylang Ylang

Anxiety
- Bergamot
- Cedar
- Chamomile
- Clary Sage
- Geranium
- Juniper
- Lavender
- Lemon

- Marjoram
- Melissa
- Neroli
- Patchouli
- Petitgrain
- Rose
- Sandalwood
- Vetiver
- Ylang Ylang

Apathy
- Cajuput
- Cedar
- Chamomile
- Clary Sage
- Eucalyptus
- Frankincense
- Geranium
- Ginger
- Lemongrass
- Lemon
- Lime

- Mandarin
- Marjoram
- Melissa
- Mint
- Neroli
- Niaouli
- Orange (bitter)
- Petitgrain
- Rosemary
- Rose
- Sandalwood
- Thyme
- Ylang Ylang

Arguments
- Bergamot
- Cedar
- Frankincense
- Geranium
- Lavender
- Mandarin
- Marjoram
- Melissa
- Myrrh
- Petitgrain
- Rose
- Sandalwood

- Thyme
- Ylang Ylang

Attachment to previous misfortune
- Cypress
- Melissa
- Rose

Confusion, indecision
- Basil
- Bergamot
- Cajuput
- Cardamom
- Cedar
- Clary sage
- Frankincense
- Grapefruit
- Mandarin
- Marjoram
- Mint
- Myrrh
- Neroli
- Niaouli
- Petitgrain

- Rosemary
- Rose
- Sandalwood
- Tea Tree
- Thyme
- Ylang Ylang

Deception

- Clary Sage
- Eucalyptus
- Frankincense
- Ginger
- Geranium
- Marjoram
- Neroli
- Niaouli
- Rose
- Thyme
- Ylang Ylang

Deep sorrow

- Chamomile
- Cypress
- Jasmine
- Lavender
- Marjoram
- Rose
- Vetiver

Depression

- Bergamot
- Chamomile
- Clary Sage
- Frankincense
- Geranium
- Grapefruit
- Jasmine
- Lavender
- Lemongrass
- Melissa
- Neroli
- Orange
- Patchouli
- Rose
- Sandalwood
- Ylang Ylang

Despair

- Cedar
- Clary Sage
- Frankincense
- Geranium
- Lemon
- Mandarin
- Marjoram
- Melissa
- Mint
- Rosemary
- Sandalwood
- Thyme
- Ylang Ylang

Despondency, discourage-ment

- Bergamot
- Cedar
- Clary Sage
- Cypress
- Frankincense
- Ginger
- Geranium
- Lemon

- Mandarin
- Melissa
- Neroli
- Niaouli
- Orange (bitter)
- Petitgrain
- Rose
- Sandalwood
- Ylang Ylang

Envy, jealousy

- Bergamot
- Eucalyptus
- Geranium
- Jasmine
- Lavender
- Lemon
- Marjoram
- Neroli
- Orange (bitter)
- Rose
- Rosemary
- Sandalwood

- Thyme
- Ylang Ylang

Fear, dread
- Clary Sage
- Cypress
- Geranium
- Mandarin
- Marjoram
- Melissa
- Myrrh
- Neroli
- Niaouli
- Orange (bitter)
- Sandalwood
- Ylang Ylang

Frustration
- Clary Sage
- Cypress
- Frankincense
- Ginger
- Lemon
- Mandarin
- Niaouli
- Orange (bitter)
- Thyme
- Ylang Ylang

Guilt
- Chamomile
- Cypress

- Lemon
- Mandarin
- Marjoram
- Niaouli
- Orange (bitter)
- Pine
- Rose
- Sandalwood
- Thyme
- Ylang Ylang

Impatience
- Cedar
- Eucalyptus
- Frankincense
- Geranium
- Ginger
- Lavender
- Lemon
- Mandarin
- Melissa
- Myrrh
- Neroli
- Orange (bitter)
- Petitgrain
- Rose
- Rosemary

Irritability
- Bergamot
- Cedar
- Chamomile

- Clary Sage
- Cypress
- Frankincense
- Geranium
- Ginger
- Lavender
- Lemon
- Mandarin
- Marjoram
- Melissa
- Orange (bitter)
- Neroli
- Niaouli
- Petitgrain
- Rose
- Rosewood
- Sandalwood
- Thyme
- Ylang Ylang

Loneliness
- Marjoram
- Rose

Low self-esteem
- Bergamot
- Cedar
- FrankIncense
- Geranium
- Jasmine
- Rose

Mood swings
- Bergamot
- Clary Sage
- Cypress
- Geranium
- Juniper
- Lavender
- Lemon
- Mandarin
- Mint
- Orange (bitter)
- Rosemary
- Rose
- Sandalwood
- Thyme
- Ylang Ylang

Negativity
- Basil
- Bergamot
- Clary Sage
- Frankincense
- Geranium
- Jasmine
- Lemongrass
- Lemon
- Myrrh
- Sandalwood

Obsession
- Clary sage
- Cypress

- Geranium
- Lavender
- Marjoram
- Melissa
- Petitgrain
- Rose
- Ylang ylang

Overly emotional, crying easily

- Cypress
- Geranium
- Lavender
- Marjoram
- Neroli

Panic

- Bergamot
- Chamomile
- Frankincense
- Lavender
- Marjoram
- Melissa
- Myrrh
- Neroli
- Petitgrain
- Rosemary
- Sandalwood
- Thyme
- Ylang Ylang

Resentment

- Rose

Shock

- Bergamot
- Chamomile
- Marjoram
- Melissa
- Myrrh
- Neroli
- Petitgrain
- Rose
- Tea Tree
- Ylang Ylang

Shyness

- Clary Sage
- Mandarin
- Marjoram
- Orange (bitter)
- Petitgrain
- Sandalwood
- Thyme
- Ylang Ylang